The
Great Sex for Life
Toolkit

I am the poet of the body,
And I am the poet of the soul.

The pleasures of heaven are with
me, and the pains of hell are
with me.
The first I graft and increase
upon myself....the latter I
translate into a new tongue.

Walt Whitman
Leaves of Grass

The
Great Sex for Life
Toolkit

A Simple Home Study Guide
to Sexual Growth and Satisfaction

Krisanna Jeffery

All Is Well Ventures Inc.
Nanoose Bay, British Columbia

Library and Archives Canada Cataloguing in Publication
Jeffery, Krisanna, 1951
    The great sex for life toolkit: a simple home study guide to sexual growth and satisfaction/Krisanna Jeffery

Includes bibliographical references.
ISBN 978-0-9782499-0-8

    1. Sex Education. 2. Sex 1. Title.

HQ31.J57 2007   613.9'6   C2006-906727-9

All Is Well Ventures Inc.
1836 Douglas Crescent
Nanoose Bay, B.C., V9P 9C7
www.greatsexforlifetoolkit.com

Editing by Miriam Shell, justwriteediting,com
Illustrations by Karen Nelson
Cover Art by Becky Baldwin

Printed in Canada
www.firstchoicebooks.ca

First Printing   2007
Second Printing   2008

To my husband, Keith, whose patience, love, and support
made the writing of this book possible.

Contents

Chapter 15
Keeping the Pot Boiling....................................195
■ So What Can We Do? ■ Creating Sexual Novelty ■ Expanding Sexual Experience ■ Maintaining Sexual Energy in Long Term Relationships ■ Exercise: Deciding Your Sexual Future

Chapter 16
When Your Pubic Hair Turns Grey.......................219
■ Myths About Sex and Aging ■ Highlights of Sex Over Fifty ■ Issues of Sex Over Fifty ■ Exercise: Dealing with the Sexual Realities of Aging ■ Troubleshooting Through the Aging Process

Chapter 17
Sacred Sex: A Lost Art....................................231
■ What Is Tantra ■ Exercise: Sacred Sex 101 ■ The Chakra Energy System ■ Exercise: Sacred Sex Self-Assessment ■ Exercise: Timeless Pleasure Hypnotic CD

Appendix A
Timeless Pleasure CD Suggestion List...................245

Endnotes...247

Preface

When it comes to sexuality, we are living in a particularly unique situation never before experienced in the history of humankind! We are living longer than ever before, but we still expect long-term monogamy from our intimate partners. Also, because of increased access to education about sex and aging, we expect to have exciting and satisfying sex well into our later years.

All of these conditions have led to an intense desire for answers to the following questions: How can we get the most joy and pleasure from our sexuality? How do we keep sexuality alive in long term relationships? And, regardless of specific relationship circumstances, what can we do to keep our sexuality vital into the later stages of life?

My experience has shown me that, culturally, people are still quite ignorant and repressed about sexual matters. Surprisingly, even in this age of free access to information, there is still very limited understanding of human sexuality. It's not that the information isn't out there to be found. The problem is more that, as a culture, we don't treat our sexuality as something important. Nor do we seem to understand that with some care and attention, sexuality is an aspect of ourselves that can grow and develop over our entire lifespan.

Over the last decade, we have heard endless political debate about the issue of same-sex marriages. Perhaps as a society, it would serve us better to be more concerned about the high frequency of no-sex (or poor-sex) marriages! It's my experience that the human condition inherently includes a fair amount of pain. So why not take full advantage of all the capacity we have for pleasure? Sex is good for our health! If we do not take full advantage of our built in pleasure system, it is a tragic, unnecessary waste.

In twenty-five years of counselling practice, I have had many frustrated clients complain about the quality of their sex lives. Many had given up on sex unnecessarily or prematurely. Special thanks go to these clients who helped me see the need for this book. They taught me that, in general, people want healthy sex lives but often don't know how to begin to deal with their sexual issues. This toolkit is an effort to fill that need.

Although all the information in this book is based on specific scientific research, this is not meant to be an academic book. Rather, it is a practical guide for anyone who wants to make the most of his or her sexual experience but who might be reluctant to ask for professional help.

The topic of adult sexuality can lead to endless cultural, political, legal, and religious arguments. My intention in this book is to stay away from taking specific positions in any of these arenas and leave sexual choices between adults where they belong...with the individuals involved.

To write this book, I have drawn on my experiences: working with couples as a therapist since 1983, as well as my participation in a number of intimate couple relationships. I thank all my clients and lovers for what they taught me. As I head into my senior years and look back over my counselling experiences and four decades of sexual practice, I contemplate lessons learned and convey them in this toolkit. It is my hope that they will help you nurture and expand your own sexuality bringing you more pleasure and joy until the end of your human experience. After all, that is your birthright!

My gratitude also goes out to other key people who encouraged and supported me in this endeavor, especially my caring husband and lover extraordinaire, Keith Jeffery. Special thanks go to my son, Simon Daniells, who was present with me at the moment of this book's inception and for his meticulous production of the Timeless Pleasure CD. Finally, I want to appreciate my good friend, Cindy Fisher, who both inspired and encouraged me.

Introduction

This book is set out in a workbook format and includes pertinent information for adults of all ages. It is not meant to be a complete encyclopedia on all sexual matters. Instead, other more comprehensive readings are recommended for information on specific topics. The goal behind this toolkit is to provide you with a means to examine your own sexual behavior and to help you determine ways you might be restricting your own pleasure. It is meant for either individuals or couples.

Each chapter discusses a different aspect of sexuality and is followed by experiential activities. If you are in an intimate relationship and you both want to expand your sexuality, you can use the book as a learning experience together. If you don't have a partner open to learning this way, or are currently single, you can do most of the exercises on your own. Our sexuality is not linked to a particular person. So the good news is that your sexuality can continue to develop regardless of your relationship circumstances.

Exercises in this book are designed to have you contemplate your sexual experience in order to provoke positive change. Many of the questions posed in the exercises are questions I would ask if you were a client wanting to expand your sexuality. But this book is not meant to replace therapy. Following these topics and doing these exercises may provoke the need for you to seek a sex therapist. If you feel stuck, please listen to that need, and seek professional help.

The *Ageless Sexuality* DVD which accompanies this workbook is a recording of one of my live seminars called *Great Sex for Life*. Its purpose is to provide a good role model for openly discussing sexual matters. It is my experience that most people are very awkward around sexual issues even with their most intimate partners. This fact alone leads to huge numbers of sexual problems. The seminar is delivered in a playful manner but the content is serious and treated respectfully.

The *Timeless Pleasure* self-hypnosis CD was included in this kit for the following reasons:

Some sexual problems stem directly from a person's inability to be relaxed enough to enjoy physical pleasure. Without being able to let go, we greatly reduce our capacity for pleasure. So Track #2 is a 10 minute self-hypnotic trance to train your body to surrender into deep relaxation.

Learning to be fully present in our bodies is another aspect of our ongoing sexual development. Tracks #3 (Body as Energy) and #4 (Chakra Connection) are designed to help you be more present and aware of your body as an energy system. Learning to monitor and manipulate your energy can greatly enhance your sexual experience.

And finally, many of us still suffer from unconscious Victorian sexual beliefs and attitudes which are still deeply ingrained in our culture. While the book deals with finding and changing those beliefs, Track #4 on the CD reinforces positive sex attitudes with healthy sexual suggestions. A list of these suggestions is located in Appendix A.

Note:

Some of the lessons in this kit will resonate with you personally, while others will not. Trust your own intuition as to which tools you think you need. I have created the template but the process is fully yours. Working with this book is a metaphor for your sex life. You decide what to do, how much, how fast, who with, and when you've had enough. Lessons which don't resonate with you now may have more meaning later.

1.

The Mystery of Sexuality

Sexuality means vastly different things to different people. Before we can start looking at how sexuality can be nurtured and enhanced, it's necessary to be clear about the topic of sexuality in general.

Lots of confusion exists around the definition of sexuality, and each person probably has their own definition and understanding of the word. Does it mean how *horny* a person gets? No, this would be considered *sex drive*. Does it describe what *turns a person on*? No, this would refer to their *sexual orientation*. Does it mean how many male or female characteristics one exhibits? No, these are issues of *biology* and *gender*. Or, does the term *sexuality* describe how sexual desires are *acted out*? No, that would describe sexual *behaviors*.

Sexuality then, while encompassing all of these aspects, is a much more global term than any of the above alone. In short, sexuality is who we are. Humans experience and express sexuality from birth to death. It is not just about how it is *acted out*. Indeed, sexuality is a major component of every person's life force. Therefore, it is well worth protecting, expanding, and cultivating.

Sexuality is how a person exists in the world all the time, not just during the act of sex. This aspect of humanity is obvious from infancy and lasts until the end of life. People are often amazed that sexual traits are so obvious at a very young age, even when parents try hard to treat children without gender bias. The fact is, children are very sexual beings. This is quite evident in the way young children pleasure themselves and find sexual games so enticing, even though they don't have specific knowledge of sex. Many adults recall having sexual dreams, masturbating, and playing sexual games as children. All those behaviors are considered part of healthy sexual development.

It is no different at the other end of life. We are acting out our sexuality until the day we die. One elderly woman told me that while her husband was having a heart attack, on their way to the hospital in the ambulance, he was sexually playful with her. Years after his death she still smiled as she fondly recalled this incident, and felt very privileged to have been the object of his sexual desire right up to the point of his death.

Apart from sexual *activity*, people tend to express sexuality in various ways through choice of clothing, how they present themselves to the world, and how they relate to others as men or women. Are we flirtatious or businesslike? Do we let our sexual energy be obvious or do we like to keep it concealed?

Are we sexually adventurous or cautious?

If we accept that our sexuality is *how we are in the world*, then maintaining or expanding our sexuality means being more fully expressive of our authentic selves, both in and out of the bedroom. It means being as alive as we can be for as long as we can. Because this takes both effort and risk, many people simply don't bother. Ask yourself whether you will be one who does?

Often, sexual partners are blamed for one's own lack of sexual energy, but in most cases it is we ourselves that have let the energy die. It is easier to blame others though, since the alternative is to take responsibility for ourselves, which always requires more effort and risk.

The effort referred to involves a commitment to personal growth—acknowledging and dealing with our feelings. **The more we repress and withhold our emotional truth from ourselves and others, the more we shut our life force down, including our sexual energy.** I have experienced this many times both personally and with my clients. It is my belief that enough of this type of emotional repression can lead to symptoms of depression, anxiety, or many other forms of dis-ease.

The risk referred to involves the risk of acknowledging our authentic feelings in order to keep our life energy flowing. Many people see that acknowledgement as a risk because as humans we tend to feel vulnerable exposing our most inner selves to others (and sometimes even to ourselves!). We have many limiting beliefs about the dangers of acknowledging our authentic feelings. And yet, we also long for the intimacy that can come from allowing ourselves to be vulnerable. Therein lies our dilemma! We want to be connected, but we fear the vulnerability of emotional honesty.

The real danger of withholding our authentic selves from others is that it can lead to loneliness and isolation. Repressing emotion reduces our energy, and ultimately, it can reduce sex drive, too. That is why, when we are feeling (or refusing to feel) resentment toward our partners, our sex drive is often diminished. For many couples, unacknowledged resentment is one of the many circumstances that can inhibit their sex drives, either temporarily or permanently. This is very sad and entirely unnecessary.

So, commitment to being as fully alive and authentic as possible is the first step to accessing and eventually maintaining healthy sexuality. As a therapist, I encourage people to make personal growth a priority in their lives. By doing so, it is very possible to create more pleasure in our lives. Isn't that a great motivator in itself?

Since you are reading this book, it is assumed that you have a desire to enhance your sex life. The first step, then, is to keep your consciousness expanding and to maintain an attitude of curiosity. Here are some questions to get you started.

Exercise: Tuning In to Your Sexuality

Purpose: To consciously explore your general sexuality.

Activity: Questions for you either to ask of yourself or to discuss with a partner.

How do you express your own sexuality in the world?

_____

_____

_____

_____

_____

_____

_____

_____

_____

_____

_____

_____

_____

_____

_____

_____

Do you feel like you are living to your full sexual energy potential?   Yes___ No___

If not, why do you think this is so?

_____

_____

_____

_____

_____

_____

On a scale of 1 to 10, what is the level of energy you have available to express yourself sexually? ____

How might you be shutting down your energy?

_____

_____

_____

_____

_____

_____

_____

What emotions are preventing you from fully expressing your sexuality?

Suggestions: anger, resentment, grief, disappointment, sadness, fear, hate, etc.

_____

_____

_____

_____

_____

_____

_____

Notes:

_____

_____

_____

_____

_____

_____

_____

_____

2.

Creating Sexual Goals

Do you think your sex life could be better? According to statistics, the vast majority of North Americans clearly state that their sex lives could be improved. However, they're not as clear on *how* their sex lives can be enhanced. Partly, that's because each of us would have a unique vision. What's yours? **We are all individually responsible for creating the lives we want, including our sex lives.** So don't just wait for it to happen. Take some action today!

This chapter creates an opportunity for you to visualize specifically what changes you want to make so that your sexuality is expressed more fully. To make any change in life, a person must make it happen. This is the phenomena of manifesting. The rules of manifestation require us first *to decide* clearly what we want. Without deciding, and then clarifying, *specifically* what we desire, change is not likely to happen. But making a clear decision with lots of energy behind it will greatly intensify the likelihood of getting what we want. Perhaps it's time for you to decide and start creating the sexual life you would prefer.

Exercise: Sexuality Visualization

Purpose: To consciously create enhanced sexual experiences.

Activity: Take some time to visualize in detail what the sex life of your dreams would look like, feel like, sound like, smell like and be like. If you are in a sexual partnership, you might consider doing this exercise separately to allow for individual input without the influence of trying to please your partner.

This process is different from fantasy. Fantasy is what you like to think about, not what you would actually like to do. For example, we might fantasize about having sex with a complete stranger because this turns us on sexually and enhances our experience with an intimate partner. However, in real life, we may not want or plan to take that risk. (see *Fantasy and Other Sexual Secrets*)

In contrast to fantasy, this process of decision making is how we actually want, and are planning, to act out our sexuality. For example, one thing you might decide is that you want to be able to be honest with your partner about your fantasy of having sex with a complete stranger. It's important to understand clearly this difference between fantasy and your desired goal because you don't want to be actively creating the life you don't, in reality, want. So, be very conscious while doing this exercise and take your time perhaps spreading it over days or weeks. This is the most important step; it is your sex life that you are creating.

I encourage you to take your manifesting very seriously!

Remember, sex starts in the mind! If it helps your process, and you feel safe doing so, write it down. This has proven to be helpful in the manifestation of goal setting of any type.

My Goals for Enhancing Sexuality

_____

_____

_____

_____

_____

_____

_____

_____

_____

_____

_____

_____

_____

_____

_____

_____

Exercise: Co-creating with Your Partner

Purpose: To take a risk and share your vision.

Activity: You have taken time to create your vision of your personalized sex life. If you are in a current sexual relationship, consider sharing your general visions with each other and see how they can fit together. Couples are often pleasantly surprised to find out that their partner wants what they also want but has been afraid to ask for it. Sometimes, other goals will require negotiation and setting personal boundaries. You may need to move on to the sexual communication chapter which can facilitate sexual discussion. Or, if you think you are ready, start making a list of general agreements in regard to what you want to create sexually.

Exercise: Sexual Goals We Agree On

Purpose: To facilitate a joint goal creation process.

_____

_____

_____

_____

_____

_____

_____

3.

When You Just Don't Feel Like Sex!

Sometimes we have the desire for sex but not the energy. Other times, we don't even have the desire. And still other times, we have the desire for sex as well as the energy but the body won't get aroused. There's no doubt about it. Sexual functioning is a complicated issue!

All of these circumstances can and will occur for each of us from time to time. But if any of the above behaviors starts to happen on a regular basis, it's time to pay attention. It's important to make the distinction between sexual desire and sexual arousal since they are two entirely different phenomena occurring in different parts of the brain. Because they are separate phenomena, they each need to be understood and treated differently.

Sexual Desire

A sexual desire concern occurs when we simply have no interest in sex. Sexual fantasies and thoughts about sex are absent. Without desire, sexual arousal is much harder, if not impossible, to achieve.

Sexual desire is a complex issue to sort out because there are many probable causes. Dr. Judith Reichman (1988)[1] reports that women are twice as likely to report desire issues compared to men, but she wonders if it's just that women can more easily admit their lack of desire. I believe this may be true because I see many men as well as women with this complaint.

Scientists admit that not much is known about sexual desire issues. But let's look at what is known. Some of the most common conditions that can affect our desire level are discussed below.

Sorting Out Sexual Desire Issues

Consider any conditions that might apply to your sexual desire.

☐ Sexual Boredom

Desire is a fundamental issue in long term relationships because the human brain craves novelty and novelty drives desire. Perhaps we have to face the fact that love isn't enough to sustain desire. We have to keep creating novel erotic experiences to keep desire for one partner sustained over a long period. Many couples have proven that a couple's sexuality can continue to expand when specific attention is paid to sexual novelty along with emotional openness and physical health. What are you doing to avoid sexual boredom? Ideas for relieving sexual boredom can be found in Chapter 15. As well, your local adult sex shop will have ideas for you. Don't be afraid to go in and browse. They won't bite!

☐ Medications

Some medications will affect sexual desire while others will allow desire but not arousal. Still others will allow both desire and arousal but will prohibit orgasm. If you are taking a new medication and think it might be affecting your sexual desire, you might want to check with your pharmacist to see if that drug could be causing a sexual problem. If so, consider talking to your doctor because sometimes other drugs can be substituted.

☐ Physical Problems

Physical problems such as disorders of the endocrine system, hormone imbalance, sexual pain disorder, and many other health issues can affect desire. If you are experiencing a lack of desire, the first step in your investigation would be a full medical check up to determine your state of health. Please don't avoid telling your doctor that you are experiencing sexual desire issues because that symptom alone is a valuable piece of information when it comes to determining what's going on inside your body.

☐ Relationship Issues

Resentment and power struggle can destroy sexual desire. In many cases, these issues have to be worked out before both partners are willing to allow their sexual desire to be experienced. In other cases, couples use their sexuality to work out such issues. While the majority of people with sexual issues don't think about asking for help, the option is always there for the more courageous. Shop for a therapist you feel comfortable with and get those issues worked out. You'd be surprised how fast your relationship can make a shift for the better.

Sexual Arousal

A sexual arousal issue occurs when the body doesn't respond to sexually stimulating fantasy, suggestion, or touch. There may be lots of desire for sex but no physical response. In women, it shows up as a lack of genital swelling and lubrication. In men, it shows up as an inability to get or maintain an erection. And it's really frustrating!

Like sexual desire, sexual arousal can be caused by many things, including all the above reasons that cause desire problems (sexual boredom, medications, physical problems, and relationship struggles). Once these reasons are ruled out I would consider some of the following causes of low arousal. Again, consider which of the following you think might require further investigation.

☐ Sexual Technique

Sometimes arousal issues can be overcome with a simple change in sexual technique. We are not born knowing how to be great lovers, and some have more of a knack for it than others. Also, because our bodies change hormonally from day to day, the same technique, no matter how good and creative it might be, will not always create the same response. As our bodies change with age, we will definitely require different types of stimulation.

Since we're not mind readers, we need feedback from our partners to really know how to please them, which is where things seem to fall apart because sexual communication is so difficult for many of us. Most of us could use improvement in this area (see Chapter 8).

Take the time to learn all you can about what turns you and your partner on, and don't make any assumptions which just get you into trouble. Consider doing the exercises in Chapter 5. They will help you learn what turns you and your partner on. In addition, a huge selection of books on the topic of sexual technique is available for you to explore.

☐ Inability to Relax

Many sexual challenges such as arousal problems, difficulty having orgasm and premature ejaculation can stem from our inability to relax adequately. The habit of not relaxing can be due to the stress of a fast-paced life, early childhood conditioning, or simply from having an anxious nature. Either way, the remedy is to retrain the body to relax. The companion CD to this book, *Timeless Pleasure,* has a self-hypnotic track designed to help you learn to relax and let go.

Learning to relax has cured many sexual challenges. It is a powerful remedy often overlooked because of its simplicity.

☐ Being in your Body

Becoming fully conscious in the body can be a problem for many people. There are numerous reasons why this might happen, but generally, it's about not wanting to fully feel human emotions. We all have this habit to some degree. We learn by an early age that one way to avoid feeling our uncomfortable emotions is to 'stay in our heads'. Since emotions are felt in the body this strategy works to some degree. However, the downside is that when we develop this habit we also inadvertently limit our pleasure potential. That affects our ability to enjoy pleasurable activities to their fullest, and certainly, it will affect the ease with which we become sexually aroused.

The CD, *Timeless Pleasure*, has two tracks called "Body as Energy" and "Chakra Connection." Both these self-hypnotic trances are designed to help you develop a stronger ability to put your consciousness more fully in your body. This in turn will create more potential for you to experience pleasure.

☐ Negative Sex Attitude

Many of us, because of our early sex conditioning, have conscious or unconscious negative sexual attitudes. Many of the exercises in this book are designed to combat such attitudes. It's very important to identify and change any limiting beliefs, because they will severely limit your pleasure potential. Chapter 4 called *Developing Your Best Sexual Attitude* delves deeply into this topic. As well, the *Timeless Pleasure* CD has a track with sex positive attitudes to reinforce healthy beliefs about your sexuality. A list of these affirmations can also be found in Appendix A.

Sexual Energy

I'm often asked, "How can I get more energy for sex?" There are many responses to this question. The most obvious being that we may simply be doing too much. My heart goes out especially to couples with young families who are living incredibly stressful and busy lives. However, young or old, if we want a better sex life we can benefit from making sex a higher priority in our lives.

If you are in that category of lovers who have sexual desire and are making sex a priority but still don't have the energy for it, then here is a checklist of some of the more common possibilities to check out:

- ✓ Low fitness level
- ✓ Depression
- ✓ Anxiety
- ✓ Poor diet
- ✓ Medications
- ✓ Adrenal exhaustion
- ✓ Hormone imbalance
- ✓ Thyroid dysfunction
- ✓ Resentment
- ✓ Sleep disturbance
- ✓ Chronic pain
- ✓ Disease

As a counsellor, I don't pretend to be a specialist in medical conditions that can affect sex drive. So for a complete discussion on improving libido caused by medical problems, see the work of Judith Reichman, MD. (1998).[2] Although her book was written for women, many of the same physical problems naturally afflict men. Hopefully, your own physician will be open to discussing sexual issues with you if the need arises. However, if you don't get the help you need on your first try, keep looking rather than just giving up. You and your sex life are too important for that!

Fortunately, many of these problems have solutions. And this is by no means a complete list of possible problems which can interfere with sexual energy, just those that I have found most common. For better sex, the physical issues need to be dealt with either through conventional or holistic medicine. Please see your health care practitioner to rule out physical problems.

Our reality is that sex can only be as good as the general health of the body. It's that simple! Without energy, flexibility, muscle tone, and hormone balance, one's ability to express sexuality through sexual activity will be greatly compromised. Luckily, we can *all* be doing activities which increase our level of wellness, no matter what the current level is. How much attention do you pay to these things? How limited is your sexual expression due to weakness in these areas of wellness?

Exercise: Exploring Sexual Desire

Purpose: If you are having trouble deciding whether you have a sexual desire issue, consider the following questions to help you determine if you want to seek help in that area. Circle the number that pertains most to you.

1   definitely not true
2   sometimes not true
3   neutral
4   sometimes true
5   definitely true

Several answers in the 4 to 5 range of the scale might indicate the need for investigation with a physician or qualified sex therapist.

I don't have sexual fantasy.
1   2   3   4   5

I don't ever initiate lovemaking.
1   2   3   4   5

I have no interest in self-pleasuring.
1   2   3   4   5

Even when my partner initiates sex, I find it hard to enjoy.
1   2   3   4   5

I'd be happy not to have sex.

   1   **2**   **3**   **4**   **5**

Sex isn't really worth the effort it takes.

   1   **2**   **3**   **4**   **5**

During sex I don't really feel present.

   1   **2**   **3**   **4**   **5**

The idea of having sex doesn't really
ever enter my mind.

   1   **2**   **3**   **4**   **5**

Am I willing to check into seeing if there are
physical reasons for any sexual desire issues?

Yes_____ No_____

If the answer is no…then, why not?

_____

_____

_____

_____

_____

_____

_____

4.

Developing Your Best Sexual Attitude

Once you have had a clean bill of health but still don't feel you have the energy for sex, then it's time to look at what psychological issues might be impacting your sexual energy. Aside from the obvious impact of negative relationships, there are also many limiting (often unconscious) beliefs that can shut down your sexuality.

Regardless of how we are brought up or how liberated we think we are, our sexual attitudes were shaped by the society in which we were raised. Parents, schools, religion, politics, and our peers have all played a role in our developing sexuality.

As I have traveled to different societies, I've seen many different cultural traditions regarding sexuality. Tolerance for various displays of female sexuality is one example. All societies have different rules about how women can show their sexuality. Here are just a few variations I've observed:

♥ In Thailand, it is not considered proper for a woman to show her ankles in a place of worship.

♥ In Japan, traditional married couples are rarely seen together in public. Physical displays of affection in public are definitely not appropriate.

♥ In some cultures, it is not ok for women to show most parts of their bodies in public, including their faces.

♥ In our own culture, only the breasts and genitals need to be covered in public.

♥ In still other cultures, it is ok for women to show their breasts in public.

So what is sexually appropriate? You will notice that **there is no consistency on sexual issues from one culture to another.** It seems that there is no one *right* way for women to display their sexuality. And of course, the same goes for men. How much of who we are sexually has been dictated by our culture and how much is authentically who we are? This book is about investigating that very question.

Clearly, there are no universal truths about sexuality because each society has differing sexual rules based on that particular culture's beliefs. Except for the basic facts of physiology, sexual beliefs are totally open to personal interpretation. It makes sense then to take responsibility for defining and deciding our own sexual beliefs. While each different culture has historical reasons for its rules about sexuality, we do not need to buy into any one culture's collective beliefs without first consciously looking at what they are. We need to ask ourselves the question: Does that belief work for me today?

Our Most Powerful Sexual Organ

If I asked you what body organ is the most powerful for satisfying sex, what would you answer? The answer is often the genitalia. But contrary to popular belief, the brain is our most powerful sex organ. Without the brain there can be no sexual response.

Ultimately it is the mind (the software) that seems to run the brain (the hardware) and consequently, our sexual experience. If you have any doubt about this fact, just try having good sex when you're really worried about something. Without the mind focused on sex, the brain cannot create a healthy sexual response. So if we want more satisfying sex, we need to be consciously aware of what's going on in the mind.

What thoughts and beliefs do you have that might be limiting your sexual experience? Many of us are not even aware of what limiting core beliefs we might have about our sexuality. This chapter will give you a vehicle to examine thoughts or beliefs which may be restricting your sexual experience. While some beliefs are obviously unconscious, focusing on your sexual beliefs may bring them more fully to conscious awareness.

Below is a list of possible limiting beliefs about sexuality. They are called limiting beliefs because they may hold you back from living your sexual potential. Most of these beliefs are based on sexual myths and are not based on any particular truths. Most will be addressed throughout this book.

You will automatically be aware of some of your limiting sexual beliefs just by reading over the following list. These beliefs are already conscious for one reason or another. However, there will be other beliefs you are not aware of because they are currently unconscious.

Unconscious sexual beliefs have power over how we live out our sexuality and are often not in our best interest. Clearly, unconscious beliefs are not always easy to discover. Applied Kinesiology, or muscle testing, can help people uncover unconscious information. If you are familiar with that particular technique or know someone who is, then this is a good place to use that skill.

If not, it is still very possible to recognize our unconscious beliefs when an effort is made. As you go through this next exercise, keep the following in mind:

Note:

♥ Please give yourself some quiet time to do this exercise because owning up to unconscious beliefs will take focus.

♥ Go over the list alone (at least at first) to make sure you are giving the exercise the required focus. Assume that you will not admit all your unconscious beliefs the first few times through the list.

♥ Expect that the part of you that resists change will sabotage this process. You may notice any of the following: avoidance, irritation, boredom, yawning, and distractions of any kind.

♥ Assume there are other limiting core beliefs that are not on this list. Jot them down as well.

♥ Highlight or check off the beliefs that you think might remotely refer to your own belief system.

♥ Later, share it with a willing partner if you wish and if one is available.

Exercise: Uncovering Limiting Core Beliefs

Purpose: To find out what beliefs might be holding you back from living your sexual potential

Limiting Beliefs about Sex in General.

☐ Sex is bad

☐ Limiting beliefs about sex can't be changed

☐ My sexuality is dangerous.

☐ I won't be loved if I allow my full sexuality to show.

☐ Sex is only for procreation.

☐ Sex is dirty.

☐ Enjoying sex is naughty.

☐ Putting attention on sex is dangerous.

☐ Sex is overrated.

☐ Only some people can have good sex.

☐ Only young people can have good sex.

☐ I need to be secretive about my sexual practices.

☐ It's not safe to experience my sexual potential.

☐ It's too late for me to achieve my sexual potential.

☐ If I really get into feeling pleasure, I might get addicted.

☐ Pleasure is sinful.

☐ Receiving pleasure is wrong/difficult/awkward.

☐ Enjoying sex makes me too vulnerable.

☐ It's not safe to ask for what I want sexually

☐ Others::

_____

_____

_____

_____

_____

Limiting Sexual Beliefs Related to Gender

☐ Men enjoy sex more than women.

☐ Women are not as sexual as men.

☐ My penis is not the right size for good sex.

☐ My vagina is not tight enough.

☐ I'll be rejected for the size or shape of my genitals.

☐ Men instinctively know how to be good lovers.

☐ Men should always be ready to have sex.

☐ Women shouldn't initiate sex.

☐ Heterosexual sex is the only kind of appropriate sex.

☐ Women should be submissive in sex.

☐ Men should be dominant during sex.

☐ Women who like sex are cheap.

☐ Women who enjoy their sexuality won't be respected.

☐ Men will leave women who are sexually expressive.

☐ Good girls don't enjoy sex.

☐ Older women are not sexual.

☐ Others:

_____

_____

_____

_____

_____

_____

_____

_____

Limiting Sexual Beliefs about your Body

☐ Only *attractive* people can enjoy sex.

☐ I'm not attractive sexually or desirable.

☐ My body isn't perfect enough to be sexually attractive.

☐ Parts of my body are not acceptable to me.

☐ Nudity is bad/wrong/immoral.

☐ Genitals are unattractive or ugly.

☐ Genitals are dirty or disgusting.

☐ Natural body odors are unpleasant.

☐ Older bodies cannot be sexually attractive.

☐ Others:

_____

_____

_____

_____

_____

Limiting Sexual Beliefs about Self Love and Deservedness

☐ I don't deserve to feel pleasure.

☐ I don't deserve to be loved.

☐ I'm afraid I'll be taken advantage of.

☐ I'm afraid I'll be used sexually.

☐ I'm not loveable.

☐ Others:

_____

_____

_____

_____

_____

Limiting Sexual Beliefs: Psychological Issues

☐ It's not safe to be sexually vulnerable.

☐ Sex is dangerous.

☐ I'll lose my identity if I let myself be sexual.

☐ It's not possible for me to enjoy sexual pleasure.

☐ I won't let myself enjoy pleasure.

☐ It's not possible for me to enjoy sex.

☐ Others:

_____

_____

_____

Limiting Sexual Beliefs about Self-Pleasuring

☐   Masturbating is bad, immoral, or dirty.

☐   My religious doctrine says masturbating is evil.

☐   If I masturbate it means I don't desire/love my partner.

☐   If I was having satisfying sex I wouldn't want or need to self-pleasure.

☐   Masturbating will create physical problems.

☐   Masturbating isn't as good as real sex.

☐   Masturbation is selfish.

☐   It's not safe to admit that I masturbate.

☐   Masturbating has to be done fast.

☐   Masturbating always has to be done in private.

☐   Masturbating isn't part of the sex act.

☐   I don't deserve to pleasure myself.

☐   It's not safe to pleasure myself.

☐   Others:

_____

_____

_____

_____

_____

_____

Limiting Sexual Beliefs about Fantasy

☐ Having sexual fantasy is not normal.

☐ We should be able to stop/control sexual fantasies.

☐ Fantasy is a predictor of behavior.

☐ Fantasies have to be private.

☐ Fantasies can't ever be acted out.

☐ Fantasies will eventually have to be acted out.

☐ It's not safe to share my fantasy life with my partner.

☐ Having fantasy about inappropriate people in appropriate ways is bad.

☐ Others:

_____

_____

_____

_____

If none of these limiting beliefs about sex relate to you, then congratulations. You don't have to read on. However, if you have found some limiting core beliefs that have been lurking in your mind, the next step is to *consciously* decide if you want to keep believing them. We are all entitled to our own beliefs of course. However, if you want to have more satisfying sex, then a critical step in the process is to examine and change the beliefs that have held you back. So if you feel ready to start giving them up, read on.

Exercise: Make a list of any limiting beliefs you feel ready to change.

Purpose: To consciously begin the change process.

_____

_____

_____

_____

_____

_____

_____

_____

_____

_____

_____

_____

_____

_____

_____

_____

_____

_____

_____

_____

Belief Changing

Do you believe that beliefs can be changed? Or do you believe that they are somehow etched in stone somewhere in your brain? The fact is that you have changed your beliefs about the world many times through your entire life.

Consider for example, when you were a wee child. You no doubt thought the world consisted of your community. Later, as you received more information and experience, you *decided to believe* that the world is your town. And later, as you received more information and experience, you began to believe that the world was your country. And so on, until you received enough information and experience to believe the world was the universe.

So you can see how easily beliefs *can* and *do* change. There is nothing to stop you from ultimately changing yours. It can be quite simple. We get new information and decide to believe something different. You've done it many times. The hard part is finding out *which beliefs are running an unconscious program* (in this case with your sexuality). And once you've done that, you can decide which core beliefs you would like to replace them with. Often the awareness of a limiting core belief alone is enough to shake it loose.

When You Need Professional Help

Realistically, it needs to be said here that it is possible for us to be so conditioned and attached to holding certain beliefs that even if part of us wants to change them, another part of us can be hanging on to them tenaciously. This is where therapy is helpful. If you know you are in this category, ask for help. Moreover, if you have limiting beliefs around asking for help (like so many do) you might as well get them treated while you're at it!

For example, let's imagine that you had the limiting core belief that *sexual desire is evil* drilled into you. **Common sense dictates that humans would not have been given sexual desire if we were not meant to use it.** So, you've admitted that this is not logical or rational. Still, you may find that you have an aversion to letting your desire surface even though you want to believe that *desire is natural to being human.*

If, after acknowledging the belief and trying to change it on your own, you find you still can't let yourself feel the full potential of your desire, then you most likely will benefit from the help of a professional who is used to dealing with changing limiting core beliefs. There are many different techniques for belief change. In particular, the field of energy psychology offers several very effective belief change strategies (See www.energypsych.org).

However, many beliefs can be changed simply with education and conscious attention. If you have isolated some limiting beliefs around your sexuality, then here's how you can start changing them.

Exercise: Changing your Limiting Beliefs

Purpose: To set a conscious and powerful intention to change beliefs

Activity: Make a list of all your negative beliefs about sex that you are now aware of. For interest's sake, have a look at where this belief might have originated. Ask yourself if this belief fits for who you are today and what you want. If it doesn't, rewrite a different belief that does fit.

Limiting Belief	Origin	New Belief
_____	_____	_____
_____	_____	_____
_____	_____	_____
_____	_____	_____
_____	_____	_____
_____	_____	_____
_____	_____	_____
_____	_____	_____
_____	_____	_____
_____	_____	_____

Reinforcing New Beliefs

Say the new belief out loud to yourself and others. Write it down. Commit to doing whatever it takes to install the new belief. One self-help technique for belief changing that you can easily learn is called Emotional Freedom Technique (EFT). I teach this simple mind-body technique to most of my clients because it teaches the body to let go of non-resourceful emotions and beliefs. While this technique doesn't lend itself to being taught in the scope of this book, it can be learned easily by video. Information on this technique can be found at www.emofree.com.

It's important to recognize that some old beliefs are not replaced easily and will reoccur for awhile. The audio CD in this kit will help with this process. Track #4 has a self-hypnotic induction filled with suggestions for allowing and enhancing healthy sexuality. A list of the affirmations used can also be found in Appendix A. In summary, expect gradual change. Look for positive sexual behavior changes. Again, at the risk of overstating the obvious, get help if you are not getting the change you desire.

5.

The Ins and Outs of Sexual Anatomy

One would think that in this information era, we would all be well acquainted with our sexual anatomy. Definitely not so! Ignorance still abounds, not just about the opposite sex, but even about our own bodies, not just among the young, but even among the elderly.

Many people, especially women (not surprisingly, due to the location of their genitals), do not have a clear understanding of their own sexual anatomy. Let's face it; it can be kind of confusing.

In most cases we don't even use proper vocabulary to discuss our body parts, often resorting to slang or ambiguous phrases like *"down there"* and *"between my legs"*. I mean really…what *have* we got against anatomically correct words?

If we want better sex, we need all the body awareness we can get. So, I encourage anyone interested in knowing their body better to learn and use the actual names of your sexual anatomy as well as to do a thorough self-exam with a mirror and a good flashlight as described on the following page.

Exercise: Don't Be a Stranger to Your Sexual Anatomy

Purpose: To be very clear about your own anatomy and what feels good for you, and to create a clear way to share this information with a partner.

Activity: Using a mirror, flashlight, and the diagrams on the next page as a guide, identify all the parts of your genitals. Note the colors and textures of all your genital parts. Women: purposefully experiment with moving the hood of the clitoris back and forth over the gland while watching consciously. Men: consciously move the foreskin (if you have one) over the head of the penis.

Obviously, you have touched yourself this way many times. But this time, watch from the mirror angle. Using the diagrams below, locate and touch all the different parts of your genitals using various finger strokes.

Both sexes can do kegel exercises with the PC muscle (see Chapter 13) while watching. This gives you a clear idea of what happens physiologically when you engage that muscle. Knowing where a muscle is located is the first step to being able to control it. And the more you can control the PC muscle the better your sex (and urinary control) will be.

While this might seem like a ridiculously simple and unnecessary exercise, I can guarantee that most people are so estranged from their genitalia that they haven't really had a good close look. Even if you did look earlier in life, look again because over time things definitely change in the genital area.

Finally, if you're interested in using this exercise to convey information to your sexual partner, you might want to color in any areas of the diagrams on the next pages, that are particularly pleasurable (or not pleasurable) to show your lover. Your partner will appreciate the concrete tips!

Female Genitals

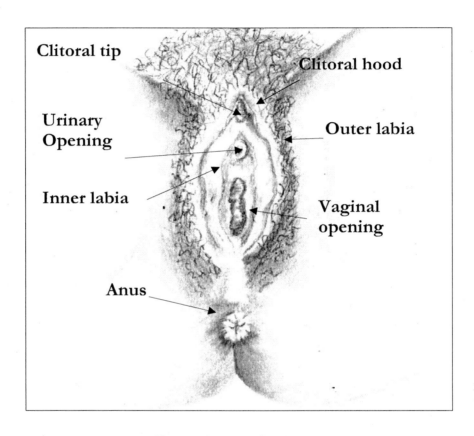

Clitoral tip

Clitoral hood

Urinary
Opening

Outer labia

Inner labia

Vaginal
opening

Anus

Illustrations by Karen Nelson, RN

Male Genitals

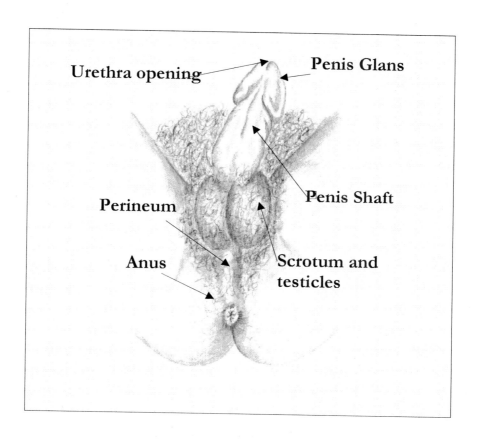

Illustrations by Karen Nelson, RN

Note: Don't do the following exercise unless you feel safe enough with your partner. If you don't feel safe, please consider getting some counselling to help change that situation.

Exercise: Partner Genital Exam (i.e. Playing Doctor)

Purpose:
To get to know your partner's body as well as you know your own.
To educate your partner about how you like to be touched.
To practise giving very specific and useful feedback.
To practise listening closely to what your partner is saying.
To take the guessing out of giving genital pleasure.

Activity: After you are comfortable examining yourself, take turns examining each other, keeping in mind the following guidelines:

Use a good light.
Make sure you each locate all the genital parts.
Use different touch and strokes, varying pressures.
Guide each other's hands.
Ask for feedback (How does this feel?).
Give clear feedback: **scale your degree of pleasure on a 1 to 10 scale**.
Remember to make clear suggestions.

The purpose is not to have sex but to educate each other. (But what the heck, let the energy move where it may!) Stay present with each other both during and after this exercise, as it is an intimate exercise to share. Make it enjoyable, not clinical.

The Sexual Response Cycle

To fully understand the arousal process, it is important to be aware of the common academic way of describing the sexual experience. This approach is based on two primary contributions to the field: the *Phases of Sexual Response* as determined by the research of Wilhelm Reich, then later by Masters and Johnson[3]. Their research gave us a way to talk about what *physically* happens during sex. They used the following clinical terms to describe the sexual response phases:

- ♥ Excitement (sexual build-up)
- ♥ Plateau (I can't wait another second)
- ♥ Orgasm (release)
- ♥ Resolution (after-glow)
- ♥ Refractory Period (the period from orgasm to our next sexual interest

Their research allowed us to have a western scientific vocabulary to describe various aspects of the physical sexual experience. That was a step in the right direction because it created more understanding. However, it also encouraged people to see sex as a linear, orgasm focused experience, which is far too narrow a view, especially as we age.

This view of sex has set up an expectation that all of our sexual experiences need to follow this model to be considered successful and satisfying. But clearly, we have many sexual experiences that do not follow the above sequence. This will be discussed more in detail in the chapter on orgasm.

Indeed, when it comes to sex research our culture is in the infancy stage. For example, it has taken centuries for the scientific community to accept the importance of women's primary sexual organ.

Female Anatomy

The Clitoris

The clitoris is the only organ in human anatomy that exists for the sole purpose of sexual enjoyment! That's proof enough for me that we were designed for pleasure. But one wonders how it was possible for the clitoris to go unacknowledged as women's primary sexual organ within western culture for so long! Although it was acknowledged for centuries in the sexual literature of other cultures, women in the west were actually discouraged from putting any importance on their clitoris.

Historically, there were several reasons why this occurred. In the Judeo-Christian culture, the beliefs about sex being only for procreation discouraged all forms of sex except penis-vagina intercourse. This pretty much eliminated any emphasis on the importance of the clitoris.

Freudian theories of female sexuality had a very strong hold on popular belief in the past century. Freud stated that the clitoris was an inferior form of a penis and that healthy women needed to move their attention (and penis envy) from the clitoris to their vagina.

It has only been since Alfred Kinsey's sex research[4] in the 1950's that science finally determined the clitoris was the key location of sexual sensitivity in women (as though women didn't already know!). Later in the 1960's, Masters and Johnson stated that all female orgasms involve the clitoris.

Even though these facts have been published many times in the past thirty years, it seems that many women still have not incorporated clitoral stimulation into their partner sex. Shere Hite (1976) stated in her well known *Hite Report*[5], a nationwide study of 3,000 women on female sexuality, that we still lack a complete understanding of women's sexual anatomy. I find this to be true today, thirty years later. This ignorance continues to create confusion and unnecessarily dissatisfying sexual practices.

Credible research has estimated that 50% to 75% of women need direct clitoral stimulation to reach orgasm during intercourse[6]. In addition, the *1994 Sex in America Survey*[7] found that less then one third of women can reach orgasm during sex with a partner. Obviously, with more direct clitoral stimulation during partner sex, the percent of orgasmic women would go up considerably. But let's look at why clitoral stimulation is so necessary for so many women.

On this topic, I quote from Edward Brecher's classic, *The Sex Researchers:*

> The truth is…that the glans and shaft of the human clitoris are merely the superficially visible or palpable manifestations of an underlying *clitoral system* which is at least as large, as impressive, and as functionally responsive as the penis…and which responds as a unit to sexual stimulation in much the same way as the penis does.[8]

The Clitoral System

Illustration by Karen Nelson, RN

So, what we normally think of as the clitoris is actually just the tip of it. In fact, the entire clitoral system is as large as the penis and when aroused, it engorges thirty times the size of the clitoral glans and shaft, like the penis. Eureka! Ladies, no more need for penis envy!

Why is this important to know? Well, in my workshops, I like to remind both men and women of the following important fact: **For women, having sex without clitoral stimulation is simply like men having sex without any stimulation of their penis. (What are the odds of that?)**

It naturally follows that for women, having sex without enough stimulation to fill the erectile tissue of the clitoris with blood would be like men trying to have sex without an erection. Even though it's possible, most men would not find it preferable.

Women have complained to me that their partners have never actually learned to stimulate their clitoris properly. When asked if they have told their partners what *properly* actually is, they usually answer no. For some reason, they have been afraid to be specific with that information, no doubt trying to spare their partner's feelings and are often not clear themselves about what they want. Clearly, this approach will not work and in the end, when sexual resentments build up and explode, feelings do not get spared.

In summary then, the clitoris is much larger than previously thought. It consists of various parts aside from what we see. The complete anatomy of the clitoris, which is made up of erectile tissue just like the penis includes:

♥   *The hood* which protects the tip's immense number of nerves. The hood usually retracts during early arousal and protects again in higher states of arousal when the tip might become oversensitive.

♥   *The tip* which is usually the most sensitive to touch (Sometimes too sensitive!).

♥   *The shaft* which extends under the skin toward the pubic bone.

♥   *The clitoral legs or crura:* where the clitoral shaft divides to form two legs which extend for about three inches along each side of the lower vagina.

For arousal to occur, blood needs to engorge the clitoris just as it does the penis. Each part of female sexual anatomy corresponds to a part of the male anatomy. You see, we are really not that different! The clitoral hood is similar to the foreskin. The clitoral tip is similar to the head of the penis. The shaft of the clitoris corresponds to the shaft of the penis.

The clitoral legs correspond to the crura of the penis. Brecher goes on to clarify…

> In short, the only difference between men's and women's erections is that men's are on the outside of their bodies and women's are on the inside. (Women) think of your clitoris as the tip of your "penis" the rest of which lies underneath the surface of your vulva---or think of a penis as just the externalization of a woman's interior bulbs and clitoral network.[9]

It is so important to clarify any confusion you might have about the vital role the clitoris plays in female sexuality. It simply cannot be ignored in order for women to have satisfying sex. I encourage women to speak up about their needs and their sexual partners to be sensitive to the information they hear or learn.

Women's G-Spot

Amazingly, science is still debating the existence of other aspects of sexual anatomy as well. I refer to the on-going debate over the infamous "G-Spot".

Given that it took centuries for the clitoris to be properly acknowledged, I am not surprised that the existence of the G-Spot is still being debated even though it's been documented in the literature of other cultures for centuries. Furthermore, those that have heard about its existence in women may still not be aware of the corresponding erogenous zone in men (see next section).

The best summary I have found of current research and description of the G-Spot was done by Cathy Winks in a very user-friendly little book called *The G-Spot*[10] (Who knew there was that much to say about it?). I highly recommend you read this book to gain a full understanding of the G-Spot.

While all the details are beyond the scope of this book, some discussion of the G-Spot is important. The female G-Spot is usually described as a spot on the forward wall of the vagina, but it is believed that the sensitivity actually originates from the urethra[11]. It was named after the gynecologist, Dr. Ernest Gräfenberg who wrote a journal article about this subject in 1950. So what is the G-Spot exactly? The use of the word "spot" was coined more by the media than by Gräfenberg himself. What he actually said was:

> Analogous to the male urethra, the female urethra also seems to be surrounded by erectile tissues like the corpora cavernosa. In the course of sexual stimulation, the female urethra begins to enlarge and can be felt easily. It swells out greatly at the end of orgasm. The most stimulating part is located at the posterior urethra, where it arises from the neck of the bladder.... An erotic zone always could be demonstrated on the anterior wall of the vagina along the course of the urethra.[12]

Dr. Gräfenberg's emphasis wasn't on a particular spot but rather, on the urethra itself. So let's have a closer look at the urethra and its function during sex.

Urethral Sponge/G-Spot

The urethra is a long narrow tube which carries urine out of the body from the bladder. If you look at the following diagram you will see the urethra is the opening between the vagina and the pubic bone.

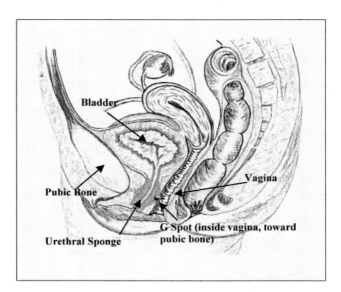

Illustration by Karen Nelson, RN

The urethra is surrounded by spongy erectile tissue called the urethral sponge[13]. It has also been referred to as the *female prostate* because it has some structural similarities to the male prostate gland. Known more commonly as the G-Spot, this tissue swells during arousal and many women enjoy having this area stimulated.

Sexology researchers still debate the particulars of the G-spot, which may be because the actual location of this area of sensitivity varies from woman to woman, and some women will not feel it at all. The important thing is, if there is an erogenous zone you have not yet discovered, you might as well discover it! For some women, it can be located through the front wall of the vagina (see diagram). Research has shown it to be much easier to locate when a woman is already highly aroused.

If you are a woman who has never experienced G-Spot stimulation, you may first want to explore on your own. During your exploration, keep in mind that every woman is different and each woman's response can vary from day to day and situation to situation. There is no *normal* response to stimulation of this area just as **there is no *normal* response for any sexual experience.** We are simply too diverse sexually for there to be any sexual response we can call "normal." Women's responses to G Spot stimulation can vary from extremely pleasurable to feeling nothing special, or even very uncomfortable.

Exercise: Finding that Female G-Spot

Purpose: To explore G-Spot stimulation in a relaxed, unthreatening scenario.

♥Empty your bladder first because initially, stimulation of the G-Spot can cause the feeling that you need to urinate.

♥Remember it will be easier to locate this spot when you are aroused and it has already become engorged. So get yourself sexually excited before you start your exploration.

♥Try squatting or lying on your back with your knees up against your chest to make the spot accessible to your fingers.

♥Use pressure not light touch.

♥Explore the front of the vaginal wall up from the pubic bone toward the cervix.

♥Feel for a ridged area that's different from its surrounding area. (It's been described as ridged, puffy, swollen, bean shaped, almond shaped, or circular shaped.)

♥If you are unable to find any erogenous spot in that area, you may want to go on to the partner experimentation. Many women report that it is much easier to locate with a partner's helping hand.

Exercise: Female G-Spot Exploration with a Trusted Partner

Purpose: Finding the G-Spot can be easier with a partner.

Activity: If you currently have a sexual partner, you may wish to do this exploration together. Proceed only if you and your partner have a trusting relationship and good communication skills.

Follow the same direction as the previous exercise but have your partner do the exploration.

♥ Give very specific feedback.

♥ Give very specific direction.

♥ Keep in mind that G-Spot stimulation can initially be uncomfortable, but with continued stimulation can become sexually exciting.

♥ Because our sensation varies daily, don't make decisions about G-Spot stimulation based on one experience. Keep exploring.

♥ Share feelings as you become aware of them and encourage your partner to do the same.

♥ Certain intercourse positions have also been reported to stimulate the G-Spot in some women. Try rear entry, or woman on top positions. It all depends on individual shape, since everyone has very different sexual anatomy.

Female Ejaculation: Fact or Fiction

Throughout history, references to female ejaculation have been made both in historical, erotic literature and in academic, anatomy texts from all over the world. For various reasons though, this phenomenon has not become widely acknowledged. In fact, within the science of sexology, it still gets hotly debated. Dr.Gräfenberg had the following to say about this topic:

> Occasionally the production of fluids is so profuse that a large towel has to be spread under the woman to prevent the bed sheets getting soiled. This convulsory expulsion of fluids occurs always at the acme of the orgasm and simultaneously with it. If there is the opportunity to observe the orgasm of such women, one can see that large quantities of a clear transparent fluid are expelled not from the vulva, but out of the urethra in gushes. At first, I thought that the bladder sphincter had become defective by the intensity of the orgasm. Involuntary expulsion of urine is reported in sex literature. In the cases observed by us, the fluid was examined and it had no urinary character. I am inclined to believe that "urine" reported to be expelled during female orgasm is not urine, but only secretions of the intraurethral glands correlated with the erotogenic zone along the urethra in the anterior vaginal wall. Moreover, the profuse secretions coming out with the orgasm have no lubricating significance; otherwise they would be produced at the beginning of intercourse and not at the peak of orgasm.[14]

Whether or not we find references to female ejaculation in our modern day anatomy texts, one thing for sure is that it is a commonly reported experience. It's hard to dispute the fact that many women themselves report that they have ejaculated a fluid from the urethra (not the vagina) during times of high arousal. We can't really argue with that!

There are no clear numbers regarding what percent of women have had this experience because sex surveys are very inconsistent. Human sexuality is so individualized that it's hard to get consistent numbers in research. Winks reports studies where the range of women reporting ejaculatory experience was from 39% to 69%[15]. Those results do not include the number of women who are convinced they are simply urinating during sex when they might actually be ejaculating.

Since there hasn't been a lot of research done on this, a lot of debate continues in current sexology literature as to what exactly this fluid is and where exactly it comes from. The studies that *have* been carried out indicate a difference in chemical make up between urine and women's ejaculate even though it comes out the urethra.[16] [17] Whatever it is, women who understand what's happening report great enjoyment from it.

Once women simply *know about the possibility* of female ejaculation, they are much more likely to have the experience. This may be because women may have already had the experience but thought (with much embarrassment) that they were urinating. After that experience, they stop themselves from the very pleasurable movement that would allow the fluid to be released. Once they redefine the experience into an erotic one, many women simply allow it to happen and enjoy it.

Not all women do (or even would want to) have this experience. I included this section to normalize some women's experiences; not to pressure others who don't experience it to think they should. There is absolutely nothing wrong with you if you don't.

Here are some points to keep in mind about female ejaculation that women have shared:

♥ The amount of fluid reported by women varies quite a bit.

♥ Sometimes it happens with G-Spot stimulation but not always.

♥ Keeping a thick towel handy might help you feel safer to experience it.

♥ Some women report that a "bearing down" movement will produce ejaculation.

♥ There has been no decision made as to this fluid's safety in regard to HIV transmission.

♥ Just because it happens once doesn't mean you'll experience it every time. Like most sexual responses, they vary with hormonal influence and many other circumstances.

Note:

With all the ambiguity about female ejaculation, we do know for sure that you can't will yourself to do it. So just be open to all possibilities. Then, if it happens, you'll know what it is. As with all aspects of sexual enjoyment, a good motto is to just allow the experience to unfold naturally and see what happens.

The Male G-Spot

It helps to understand sexual anatomy better if we realize that the sex organs of both sexes were developed from the same embryonic tissue and were identical until a certain time in early fetal development. So it stands to reason that there is a corresponding spot in men to the G-Spot in women. That spot is the prostate gland and is sometimes referred to in sexology literature as the male G-Spot. It has the potential to be an erogenous zone and some men find the stimulation of this spot very pleasurable (Perhaps not the way your doctor does it!).

Some feel it can be stimulated from the outside of the body by pressing on the area between the base of the penis and the anus, or more commonly, through the front wall of the rectum, a few inches in. Stimulation of this spot will result in indirect stimulation of the root of the penis and many men enjoy the sensation immensely. Some report a different kind of orgasm from this sort of stimulation.

In the diagram on the next page, you will see where the prostate is located. Its size is about that of a walnut. As with women, it may be hard to locate the spot yourself. I recommend the same exercises for finding the male prostate as I did for the female G-Spot.

Keep in mind that anal penetration is an activity that requires careful consideration in terms of cleanliness, lubrication, safe sex, and emotional vulnerability. This is discussed in the next section on anal stimulation.

Male Sexual Anatomy

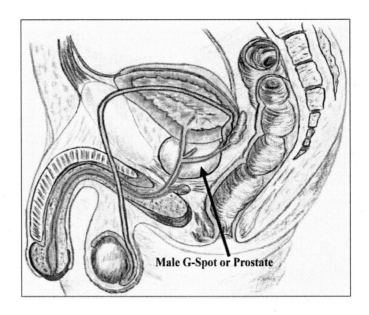

Male G-Spot or Prostate

Illustration by Karen Nelson

The Anus as a Sex Organ

The last part of sexual anatomy to discuss in this chapter is the anus. (I can feel some of you squirming already!) Most of us have been conditioned in our early childhood to have a negative attitude toward our anus. Many think of the anus as "dirty" and "disgusting." **Nevertheless, the fact remains that the anus is loaded with nerve endings and many people find anal stimulation as arousing as genital stimulation.**

If you are one of those people who have decided to incorporate anal stimulation into your sex life, then you've already overcome your early negative conditioning about this part of your body. That always deserves acknowledgement.

If you do not intend to incorporate your anus into your sexual pleasure that's perfectly fine as well. As with all sexual activity, you have the clear and unequivocal right to choose what you like. It's very important that you don't let yourself get pressured into any sexual activity you don't want.

On the other hand, you don't want to limit your sexual pleasure due to negative conditioning either. So I simply invite you to do an attitude check on this particular topic by completing the following exercise.

Exercise: Anal Attitudes

Purpose: To be conscious and clear about your beliefs and attitudes about incorporating the anus into sexual activity so they can be explored and shared openly with your partner.

Activity: Do the following sentence completion without too much conscious thought and see what come out.

My anus is...

_____

_____

_____

_____

The idea of someone touching my anus is...

_____

_____

_____

When I think of touching my partner's anus, I feel...

_____

_____

_____

When I think of my partner using finger penetration of my anus I feel...

_____

_____

_____

When I think of anal intercourse, I think...

_____

_____

_____

_____

Oral-anal stimulation is...

_____

_____

_____

What I like about anal stimulation is...

_____

_____

_____

_____

What I don't like about it is...

_____

_____

_____

_____

The limits I want to clearly state at this time on anal
stimulation are...

_____

_____

_____

_____

_____

_____

_____

_____

_____

_____

_____

_____

_____

_____

If you are someone, who is thinking you might like to experiment with anal stimulation in your sexual activity there are, of course, special considerations. You can begin by experimenting on your own or invite your partner to help. A lot will depend on your relationship and your attitudes toward anal stimulation.

♥ Care must always be taken not to go from the anus to the vagina. Bacteria that are normal and healthy for the anus can cause problems in the vagina and the mouth.

♥ Whether you are using finger penetration, sex toy, or penis you will need lots of lubrication.

♥ Use all your sexual communication skills to avoid unnecessary discomfort.

♥ Go very slowly, as anal penetration can be uncomfortable at first and then usually gets more erotic.

♥ As always, the rules of safe sex need to be applied using condoms, latex gloves, and dental dams (see Chapter 9)

6.

Getting a Grip on Masturbation

When you hear the word masturbation, what do you feel? Common emotional responses are embarrassment, awkwardness, and even shame. Very few of us will fall unabashedly into a conversation about our self-pleasuring habits. Even though masturbation is a common, universal human sexual experience, it is still largely a taboo topic in western society. While early artifacts from some cultures depicted a positive acceptance of sexual self-pleasuring, artifacts from other cultures did not. At different times over the centuries, masturbation has fallen both in and out of favor.

The history of masturbation taboos in different societies can be fascinating because of their extreme differences. Some cultures have had strict taboos against it, while others have taught their children to masturbate as a self-soothing method.

How open are you about masturbation? According to sex research, most people masturbate. However, because of our cultural attitude toward it, we still like to hide the fact that we do it, even from our intimate partners! Sometimes knowing where our cultural beliefs come from changes our own beliefs and behaviors. So if you are a history buff and are interested in learning how we got to have such guilt and shame about this natural human experience, then read on.

The Development of the Western Masturbation Taboo

It's believed that the taboos surrounding masturbation may have been based on the idea that the bigger the tribe, the safer it would be. In the days of high infant mortality and short lifespan, any threat to survival of the tribe would need to be discouraged. Therefore, anything that reduced the odds of procreation (i.e. masturbation, homosexuality, anal sex, and oral sex) would be frowned upon. This makes perfect sense for tribal times. While obviously this doesn't still apply to our current overpopulated planet, many people still hold deeply ingrained beliefs that made sense only in the past.

In some areas of the world masturbation is still forbidden and is considered a punishable offence. Some cultures still carry out the barbaric acts of castration and clitoral surgery in order to reduce sexual pleasure. And even though North Americans see themselves as progressive, it's only been in the past few decades that we have begun to improve our own attitudes toward masturbation. It wasn't until 1940 that a respected pediatric text, *Diseases of Infancy and Childhood*[18] saw the need to remove a discussion on the perils of masturbation from its "Functional and Nervous Disorders" chapter. After a long fight by sex researchers and others, ideas about masturbation have certainly changed (although not yet nearly enough). Now, we have come full circle, and because of overpopulation, STD's, and the AIDS epidemic, masturbation is being marketed by health authorities as a *safe sex* activity.

But where did masturbation get its bad press in the first place? In western Europe, masturbation attitudes were strongly influenced by the Judeo-Christian tradition. Several key figures (e.g. the Apostle Paul, Augustine, and Thomas Aquinas) contributed to negative attitudes about the body and pleasure in general.

Interestingly enough, the one Bible scripture often quoted to condemn masturbation (Genesis 38) actually refers to a case of premature withdrawal during intercourse, not masturbation at all. Historically, there was once a belief that sperm was finite and should never be wasted. Of course, now we know that one teaspoon of ejaculate could populate a large country! But in this scripture, God was displeased that sperm was *spilled on the ground.* And for thousands of years, premature withdrawal and masturbation were painted with the same judgmental brush.

Even though Christianity has been a part of creating anti-masturbation taboos, it's my understanding that there are actually no anti-masturbation references in the Bible. There has been, however, an established philosophical trend in Christianity toward seeing the physical and the spiritual as conflicting forces. Therefore, within Christian philosophy, masturbation being a non-essential physical activity had to be discouraged in principle.

While many religions, not just Christianity, condemned sexual self-pleasuring, not all societies saw it as harmful. There are quite a few cultural exceptions to the masturbation taboo. One example can be found in the history of some North American Native cultures where, in some societies, parents not only allowed their children to masturbate, they actually taught them *how* to pleasure themselves[19]. This behavior occurred in striking contrast to modern times when in 1994, a Surgeon General of the U.S.A, Dr. M. Joycelyn Elders, reported that she was asked to resign by President Clinton for saying "masturbation is part of human sexuality and a part of something that perhaps should be taught"[20]. Apparently, to teach that masturbation is a healthy human behavior would mean we'd have to admit we do it!

In Europe, in the 18th and 19th centuries, medical and moral literature began to link masturbation with mental and physical disorders, including insanity, epilepsy, mental retardation, and a huge number of other health problems. Masturbation became a convenient target for many problems that medical science didn't understand. One reference quotes that **over 60% of medical and mental problems were blamed on masturbation.**[21] Of course other causes for all these problems were eventually found, but meanwhile, the war against self-pleasuring quietly raged on with no evidence to support it.

The idea that masturbation was dangerous was compounded by the Swiss physician, Dr. Samuel Tissot, who believed that any sexual activity, but especially masturbation, caused blood flow changes that cause nerve damage and insanity[22]. Tissot's ideas were spread by an English urologist,

William Acton. The word traveled quickly from physician to Victorian parents who apparently tried very hard to stop their children from masturbating in order to save them from blindness, insanity, and damnation. His ideas were picked up by the influential Dr. Benjamin Rush, (signer of the Declaration of Independence), who wrote several influential anti-masturbation articles which spread masturbation fears in the US.

It wasn't only men who entered the fight against masturbation. One of the contributors of Victorian thinking about sexuality was Dr. Elizabeth Blackwell. She emphasized that shame is a significant characteristic of human sexuality and thought that the goal of sex education should be to intensify shame. Like so many other physicians of her time she was obsessed with giving warnings of the dangers of male masturbation which she termed "self-abuse". Although she didn't recommend punishment of child masturbators like many before her, she did counsel parents to seriously tell their children that masturbating may make them ill.[23] The fear of masturbation became so great that society created many horrible and abusive mechanical devices, genital surgeries, and forms of discipline designed to discourage it.

European fears of masturbation spread wildly to the US. Between the years 1856 and 1932, the U.S. Patent Office awarded thirty-three patents for anti-masturbation devices. Many bizarre and barbaric strategies were tried in vain to discourage the natural act of self-pleasuring. Most of them were geared to boys but female masturbation was also discouraged. Some girls were made to wear abrasive gloves to bed which would cause pain if they touched their genitals.

In the 1800's Sylvester Graham, (inventor of the Graham cracker), and the cereal entrepreneur, John Harvey Kellogg, got very involved in the sexual behaviors of the country. They followed the Victorian sexual belief that people had an excess of sexual desire. They both believed that sex for anything but reproduction was extreme. They were also part of a health food crusade based on the idea that excess sexuality was caused by rich and spicy foods. Masturbation, erotic dreams, and frequent intercourse (more than once a month), were all considered excessive. **The Graham Cracker and Kellogg's Corn Flakes were originally designed to promote health and decrease sex drive.**

A little later, Richard von Krafft-Ebing from Germany wrote about all manifestations of sex, including masturbation, as a loathsome disease. What was most harmful about his work was that he insisted that masturbation was a factor in all sexual deviations and perversions[24]. His terrifying book, *Psychopathia Sexalis* (1886) was responsible for spreading the idea of sexual desire as a disease from generation to generation throughout the world. It was a very popular book with many editions over the years. It was last reprinted as recently as 1999 as a testimony to its ongoing influence.

The next in line of influential anti-masturbationists was Sigmund Freud (1856-1939). He believed that persuading his patients to stop masturbating might cure their neurosis[25] (Wow, did he have that wrong!). Consequently, he continued to spread this negative outlook on masturbation throughout his career until 1926, not long before he died.

One of the first hints that attitudes about masturbation were starting to change in the medical world was through the work of Theodoor Hendrik van de Velde (1873-1937). He wrote a book called *Ideal Marriage* (1926) which was just liberal enough to begin to lead the masses away from their ingrained Victorian thinking on sexuality. On the subject of masturbation he even went so far as to say that if a husband couldn't bring his wife to orgasm, then it was all right for her to perform "auto-therapeutic measures" which meant self stimulation. In those days this was obviously close to heresy, but way to go Theadoor!

A woman who contributed to a more positive attitude toward female masturbation was gynecologist, Dr. Helena Wright. She joined the fight against Victorian repression of women's sexuality in the 1920's by instructing women to clinically observe their clitoris, to learn, and then show their husbands the exact rhythmic friction needed to achieve orgasm. She had a very specific plan to help women regain their innate ability to enjoy sexual pleasure through masturbation and eventually through coitus as well.[26]

The Kinsey Reports (1948 & 1953)[27] were the first extensive studies of human sexuality. This research is still referenced today as the most reliable and extensive data available. He essentially demystified masturbation and brought it out of the closet. He found that 92% of men and 62% of women admitted to masturbating, with women tending to start later in life. He demonstrated that both intercourse and masturbation were activities carried out as much for pleasure as for procreation.

Naturally, Kinsey's research created a great deal of controversy on many levels. He showed that people that are more educated see masturbation in a more positive light, and in fact, it was the first time masturbation was described as beneficial. He also challenged many other myths about self-pleasuring. **Kinsey found that masturbation was a supplement to intercourse for many people and that there is a high incidence of masturbation in people who**

are in sexual relationships as well as in single populations.

Following Kinsey, in the 1960's Masters and Johnson also revealed that masturbation was practically a universal behavior in North America and it was practised by all ages, races, genders, and social classes. In all, 694 participants took part in their laboratory research of sexual activity. Ten thousand orgasms were observed and recorded during this research.[28] They studied many subjects during the act of masturbating and described the mechanical process of arousal through self-stimulation to be virtually the same as during intercourse. Part of their data showed that of the 204 women in their sample who were unable to reach orgasm through masturbation, 94.5% were also unable to reach orgasm through any other means. This data was interpreted by Brecher (1969) to mean that many women who never learned to masturbate were cut off from all orgasmic experience. He added:

> This close association between female inability to masturbate to orgasm and female inability to reach orgasm in marital coitus seems to be one of the most damning indictments of the Victorian masturbation taboo in the entire history of sex research.[29]

Shere Hite's reports[30] from the 1980's discuss all aspects of masturbation openly and unabashedly. While almost all of her research participants admitted to masturbating, the overwhelming majority of them were secretive about the fact that they did it. **Masturbation habits are still kept secret even from intimate sexual partners by the vast majority of people, which demonstrates the far-reaching effects of Victorian sexual shame.**

In the *Kinsey Institute New Report on Sex* (1990)[31], June Reinisch takes the topic of masturbation to a new level and discusses its many health benefits and its beneficial use in achieving orgasm for both men and women during partner sex. Although this would indicate that we have made great progress toward getting back to our natural sexual natures, we still apparently have a long way to go!

The Many Benefits of Self-Pleasuring

Well you can see that with a history like we've had, it's a wonder any of us are able to enjoy our bodies at all! More and more research is coming out that is contrary to old masturbation taboos. This research points out the many health benefits of masturbation. For example:

♥ We now know that for women, self-pleasuring increases their odds of being orgasmic (A big plus!). The *Hite Report* found that statistically, masturbation increases woman's ability to orgasm in general, as well as their ability to orgasm during intercourse.

♥ Masturbation is a great workout for the PC muscles. When these muscles are toned we have better on-going bladder and orgasmic control

♥ Several studies have shown that for men, masturbation is good for keeping the prostate gland healthy.

♥ Calories are burned during masturbation

- ♥ Positive neuro-transmitters known to boost the immune system and create positive moods are created during masturbation

- ♥ We get to know our body's responses through masturbation and can let our lover know what arouses us and therefore get the most out of lovemaking.

- ♥ We can learn orgasmic control through masturbation, thus allowing orgasmic energy to build for more intense experiences

- ♥ Masturbation is a much healthier tranquilizer than a sleeping pill.

- ♥ No one has become pregnant or diseased by masturbation

Exercise: Self-Pleasuring with Self-Love

Purpose: To bring to the surface any negative self-pleasuring attitudes.

Activity: Plan a self-pleasuring event with yourself where you consciously masturbate in a loving manner. Some ideas to get your imagination going:

♥ Book off lots of time

♥ Choose a soothing environment

♥ Use your favorite music

♥ Use any form of erotica that works for you

♥ Use oils and lotions

♥ Be loving

♥ Stretch the experience out as long as possible

♥ Go for more than one type of orgasm

♥ Have fun!

Consciously observe yourself during your self-pleasuring. Are you rushing? Are you willing to sink fully into the experience? Are you frustrated? Are you afraid you'll get caught? Are you able to really enjoy yourself? Are you thinking you're not worth all this fuss? What other self-judgments are going on? If you think it would be helpful write about your experience

If you and a partner are working on sexuality issues together, consider sharing your observations.

Self-Pleasuring Observations

_____

_____

_____

_____

_____

_____

_____

_____

_____

_____

_____

_____

_____

_____

_____

_____

_____

_____

_____

_____

_____

_____

_____

_____

_____

Can We Masturbate Too Much?

Some people ask if you can masturbate too much. In fact, historically, one of the justifications for the masturbation taboo was the idea that it was addictive. Pleasurable activities of any sort produce neuro-chemicals that make us feel good. We can easily start to crave that feeling and want it more and more. The truth is that anything can be addictive. Food for example can be very addictive. But that doesn't mean we shouldn't eat.

An addictive personality can become addicted to any behavior. My years as an addiction counselor taught me that the secret to avoiding addictions is not in the avoidance of the behavior but in treating the cause. So with food addicts we don't expect them to avoid eating, but instead look to the feelings that drive them to over eat in the first place. The same would be true of someone who felt they were masturbating compulsively, which in my own clinical experience has been extremely rare.

How Much Is Too Much?

Another common question on this topic is how would I know if I was masturbating too much? My answer is the same as it would be about any behavior. **If you feel that a behavior is having a negative impact on your life and you do it anyway, then it has become a compulsive behavior.**

We have to decide for ourselves if a behavior is having a negative impact on our lives or not. With masturbation, some examples of negative impact could be if you are:

♥ Using it often to avoid doing something less pleasurable than having an orgasm (which in my opinion would be just about everything!).

♥ Replacing sex with your partner to avoid intimacy.

♥ Avoiding difficult feelings that eventually need to be faced.

♥ Hurting yourself (I was in a Tantra Workshop once where one of the participants had masturbated so much that he'd created friction sores on his penis. It is possible to overdo touching such delicate tissue).

The answer to the question, "Am I doing it too much?" has to be left with each individual. You decide whether a behavior is creating negative impact or not. No one else can. On that note, if you do find that you have a compulsive behavior of any kind which is hurting you in any way…please get some help and get back in charge of your life.

Apparently, Woody Allen once said, "Don't knock masturbation. At least it's sex with someone I love." In short, many of the benefits we get from sex we also get from masturbating. If we let go of our guilt and shame about it and pleasure ourselves in a loving way…well then, we can even get love. Why not?

Self-Pleasuring During Partner Sex

The final point to be made about masturbation is that it doesn't always have to be a lone activity. In fact, many couples incorporate pleasuring themselves when they are having sex together. Masturbation can be a supplement to sex with a partner, not always a replacement. There are many practical applications for doing so. Here are a few examples where self-pleasuring during partner-sex comes in handy:

♥ You want to show your partner what turns you on.

♥ You want to share one of your most personal and erotic activities as an act of love.

♥ You want to stretch yourself and do something "edgy" and erotic.

♥ Your partner is fatigued during sex with you, and you want to take responsibility for your own orgasm.

♥ You just aren't getting the rhythmic friction you need to orgasm any other way, and you're ready to orgasm.

♥ Your partner is aroused by "voyeurism" and is excited by watching you self-pleasure.

♥ You and your partner enjoy masturbating yourselves while simultaneously stimulating each other.

The list goes on, but I'm sure you get the point by now. Masturbation can be a big part of sex with your partner, but if a person is too hung up about self-pleasuring, they won't be able to add this dimension to their lovemaking. This will create a sexual handicap that often stems from unconscious beliefs about masturbation.

Earlier in this book, you were invited to examine your core beliefs about masturbation. If you're not sure if you have any left over cultural guilt and shame about masturbating, consider the following exercises:

Notes:

_____

_____

_____

_____

_____

_____

_____

_____

_____

_____

_____

_____

Exercise: Playing Alone Together

Purpose: This exercise is a final test for self-pleasuring inhibitions as well as a good opportunity to stretch past your comfort zone. Stretching in this sort of way adds energy and passion to your life. Avoiding challenging experiences ultimately shuts your energy down, both sexually and otherwise. So the invitation is here to take or leave.

Activity: If you haven't ever masturbated in front of a sexual partner, I invite you to consider doing so.

Discuss with your partner what you would like to do.

Perhaps your partner would like to do it also, but it's not necessary. If you think it will be too difficult, then you can do it in stages, going a little further with it each time until you eventually can bring yourself to orgasm.

Journal and/or share what these experiences are like for you.

_____

_____

_____

_____

_____

_____

_____

_____

Notes:

_____

_____

_____

_____

_____

_____

_____

_____

_____

_____

_____

_____

_____

In closing on this subject, it is my sincere hope that some light has been shed on any repressive Victorian beliefs about masturbation that might still be unknowingly lodged in your unconscious mind. It is my heartfelt desire that the self-pleasuring taboos discussed in this chapter stop being passed on from parents to children. May you and your descendents enjoy your bodies as they are designed to be enjoyed.

7.

Fantasy and Other Sexual Secrets

Everybody has sexual fantasies, but how many people can be honest and open about them? Well, that's a different matter. And what difference will it make if we are open or secret about them? These are all more important questions than you might think.

Fantasies can greatly enhance our sexuality or they can shut it down. It all depends on what our beliefs are about fantasy and how we handle them. Certainly, having them can be a great turn on, but feeling as if we have to keep them secret from our sexual partner can reduce our sexual functioning over time. That's because withholding of important thoughts and feelings in general can create distance in our intimate relationships, and this is true of sexual fantasies as well.

Sharing of fantasies can also greatly *enhance* our sexual relationships if we have the courage to expose ourselves. When we remember that intimacy is enhanced by sharing our feelings in general, it naturally follows that we reduce our chances for intimacy when we withhold our thoughts and feelings about our innermost sexual fantasies.

Unfortunately, the concept of fantasy is greatly misunderstood and consequently our sexual fantasy lives can often become shrouded in secrecy. The culture in which we live has a huge bearing on our beliefs about what is appropriate to think about and what is not. This is unfortunate because my experience has shown me that there is a big price paid for keeping sexual secrets. **Our sex lives and intimate relationships can be negatively affected by our secrets, sexual and otherwise.** But we usually don't recognize this important connection. I'll attempt to make the association between sexual secrets and sexual energy more clear in the following few pages.

As with most other aspects of sexuality, fantasy also comes with its share of myths. Here are a few to think about.

Myth: Fantasy is a predictor of reality.

There is absolutely no proof of this. People have wild fantasies all the time, but do not wish to act them out in real life. They are a normal and healthy psychological outlet. Fantasy is a place where we do not have to adhere to the morals and rules of the culture. That's why we have them.

Myth: If we have a fantasy about something, we are ready and willing to actually do it.

For everyone but a few extremely mentally ill people, fantasy is simply what we enjoy thinking about. It is *not* necessarily, what we want to actually do. It's the one place in our lives where we can have what we want without consequence. The belief that others will think that fantasy is what we'd really like to do is one of the things that makes it difficult to share our fantasies with our sexual partners.

Myth: Sharing our sexual fantasies with our partners is dangerous.

Many partners will be turned on by your fantasies and your willingness to share them. Others would simply rather not know. There is no right or wrong way to handle this issue. But find out what your partner's wishes are in the fantasy department. If you are in relationship with a very judgmental partner, then there may be reason to worry about being judged. However, if you are seeking to improve your sex life with that partner, then your feelings about being judged will eventually need to be addressed. In evolving healthy relationships, sharing is a safe thing to do.

Myth: The content of fantasy is self-explanatory and can be taken at face value.

No, most fantasies are an attempt to satisfy a basic emotional need. For example, in the case of a rape fantasy, it could be that the person having the fantasy of being raped may be satisfying a need to be fiercely desired or loved.

Or someone having the fantasy of raping may be satisfying a need for more power over their own lives. It may be a conscious or unconscious need, but the bottom line is that fantasy is an attempt to meet our needs and is a normal healthy psychological mechanism. Having a rape fantasy does not mean we are on our way to being a rapist or asking to be a victim!

If you are a person who shares fantasy easily, then you can congratulate yourself and skip the rest of this chapter because you have not fallen for the cultural beliefs surrounding this topic. But if you are timid about sharing sexual fantasy, then I invite you to take a moment to look at perfectly understandable fears people like you might have about this level of sharing. The following exercise will help you determine the basis for fears about sexual fantasy sharing and give you a beginning place for discussion with your lover. Consider and own which fears apply to you.

Exercise: Sexual Sharing Hang-ups

Purpose: To become consciously aware of where fantasy sharing hang-ups come from.

Activity: Highlight which points apply to you.

♥ I was taught early in life that in order to survive (i.e. be accepted by my love sources), I needed to hide my sexual thoughts and behaviors.

♥ I think what I fantasize about makes me weird/bad/evil.

♥ Because society still says in many ways that sex is bad, if I am having sexual fantasies, then I must be bad.

♥ I believe that secrecy in relationships is natural; we are taught to lie early in life.

♥ I've had no modeling for fantasy sharing and don't know how to start.

♥ I think that my partner will judge me for having sexual fantasies.

♥ I think my partner will be jealous of my sexual fantasies.

♥ I don't think my partner can handle it emotionally. (In this case, we think we are taking care of them but we are really protecting ourselves.)

♥ I don't want to be seen as perverted. (Have you fallen for the cultural mistaken and limiting belief that sex is bad?)

♥ I'm afraid to have my partner know me that well.

♥ Withholding secrets makes me feel powerful; divulging them makes me feel vulnerable.

If you are in a sexual partnership or have a close friend with whom you would feel safe exposing your *feelings* about sexual fantasy, then consider doing the following exercises.

Exercise: Fears about Sexual Fantasy Sharing

Purpose: To acknowledge your fears about sexual fantasy openly.

Activity: Discuss with your partner your own feelings about sharing sexual fantasy. At this point, you are not being asked to actually share these fantasies (or the fact that perhaps you might not be having any at this time). *Just explore how you are feeling about the prospect of sharing them.*

Do any of the above fears ring a bell for you? Or do you have other fears you can share. If it's helpful to you, jot down any fears that you have identified for discussion.

_____

_____

_____

_____

_____

_____

_____

_____

_____

Exercise: Open Discussion on Sexual Fantasy

Purpose: Fantasy sharing can happen more easily if we have shared our general feelings about the topic first.

Activity: Have an open discussion with your sexual partner or a close friend, and use the following questions as a guideline. If it's helpful, make notes first.

♥ Do you have sexual fantasies?

♥ Do you recall when you started having them?

♥ Have you ever shared them? With whom?

♥ What judgments do you make about your own or others' sexual fantasies?

♥ Where do you draw the line with what kind of fantasy is acceptable and why?

♥ Do you believe it's safe to disclose your fantasies?

♥ Why or why not? When?

♥ How does it feel talking about it now?

♥ Do you see any value in sharing sexual fantasies with your intimate partner?

♥Are you open to hearing the sexual fantasies of your partner?

♥Do you think you can listen to sexual fantasy without judgment?

Exercise: The Nitty Gritty of Sexual Fantasy Sharing

Purpose: To help you get down to it!

Activity: If you feel safe in doing so, share some or all of the sexual fantasies you have had, or are currently having. If you are not used to this level of sexual honesty, this can only be done when you are ready, at your own pace. If you choose to do this exercise, you can make the process more conscious by considering the following questions:

How much were you able to be honest and forthcoming?

_____

_____

_____

_____

_____

_____

Did you censor your answers? If so, why?

_____

_____

_____

_____

_____

How did you feel disclosing your sexual fantasies?

_____

_____

_____

_____

_____

How did you react to your partner's disclosure?

_____

_____

_____

_____

_____

Thank your partner for their courage and willingness.

Other Sexual Secrets

Fantasy is not the only thing that sexual partners can withhold from each other. There are many other aspects of our sexuality that we can keep secret, such as our sexual preferences, past sexual experiences, childhood sexual abuse, affairs, attractions, arousal patterns, sexual performance anxiety, sexual health issues and lying about orgasm. If you are trying to have an intimate relationship, there is a huge cost for all of these forms of withholding thoughts and information.

In relationships in which we are building and maintaining intimacy, it's important to recognize what it is we give up by keeping secrets of any kind. I have explained to my clients many times, that each time we withhold a secret in our intimate relationships, we cut off a piece of the relationship. One small piece may not be noticed. But eventually, they add up and before we know it the trust, energy and passion has disappeared. We are often left confused, wondering what happened to our relationship. We rarely associate our deteriorating relationship with our own withholding of honestly sharing ourselves in the relationship. Another very important example of sexual secret keeping is the *sexual affair.*

Sexual Affairs: To Tell or Not To Tell

How honest can we be in relationships? This is a very common concern among couples striving for intimate relationships.

The incidence of sexual affairs is remarkably higher than we would like to think. Over the years, I've been asked many times, "Should I tell my partner about my sexual affair?". Although dealing with this issue is a common theme in couple counselling, I do not *advise* a client to tell their partner about an affair, even if I believe that to be the best course of action. However, I always give the following information to help clients make their own choice.

Secrets can be very destructive, whether the topic is abuse, addiction, or sexual affairs. Secrets within families are responsible for many of our psychological and emotional problems. With secrets in the way, family problems do not get addressed. When they don't get addressed, they can fester from one generation to another.

In general, secrets carry very negative energy into our relationships. Because of the constant worry (conscious or unconscious) about being *found out*, secrets have the potential to create neurotic behaviors or make us physically ill.

In regard specifically to sexual affairs, there are other factors to consider. **The fact that the affair occurred in the first place often indicates a lack of intimacy in the relationship.** That's one of the causes of extramarital affairs. In some cases, people hope to find missing closeness by going outside their intimate relationship. But we rarely do find the closeness we seek, because the capacity for intimacy lies within *our own ability to be open and honest with ourselves and others.* So, searching for another partner to meet this need rarely works. Adding another secret to withhold only creates more distance in the relationship.

Before deciding whether or not to come clean about a sexual affair, it's advisable to think through the consequences. For example, it's important for people to understand that telling about an affair can cause the end of a relationship. Obviously, this is a very difficult choice to make, especially where children and finances are involved. On the other hand, I don't believe the relationship can evolve and become healthy with secrets in the way. Usually, people already are aware of this. That's what brings the subject up to the counsellor in the first place. Deep down, most of us know the inherent destructiveness of secrets and lies.

Sometimes, when the above information is understood, people decide in favor of truth and are willing to face the consequences of their behavior. They don't do this because of what I've said, but because living with secrets and lies is simply too difficult. They choose to live in truth with the hope it will lead to deeper intimacy, and I commend the courage necessary to do this.

At other times, people opt to stay trapped in their secrets. They accept that the consequence of this will be a more distant relationship. They decide to settle for less intimacy in order to reduce the risk of possibly ending their relationship. I always honor both choices, because my goal is to help people make more informed and conscious choices in their lives.

Deciding to tell or not is confusing because we think we're withholding to protect the relationship, but at the same time we are likely destroying our chances of deepening it. Then one day, we wake up and sense that the relationship has gone stale. What went wrong? we ask.

Let's use the example of lying about orgasm. I believe this is a bigger issue than one would think. Statistically, over half of women have admitted to having lied about orgasm. They say they do it to protect their partner's feelings (partners who are apparently way too orgasm-focused). This may seem innocent enough, yet it changes the energy of a relationship considerably. In my sex education seminars I always ask how many people would prefer not to be lied to about orgasm, and usually everyone puts up their hand. It's my opinion that we never really ever get away with a lie. Energetically, it infects the relationship, whether we want to admit it or not! And it spreads—like a disease.

Exercise: Hard Questions about Sexual Secrets

Purpose: To help you assess your own behavior around secret keeping.

Activity: Answer the following questions honestly.

Are you in the habit of keeping secrets in your close relationships?

_____

_____

_____

If so, where did you learn that habit?

_____

_____

_____

Is this the way you want to continue to be in your intimate relationship?

_____

_____

_____

_____

_____

_____

What change are you willing to commit to from this time forward?

_____

_____

_____

_____

_____

_____

_____

_____

Notes:

_____

_____

_____

_____

_____

_____

_____

_____

_____

Go for it!

8.

Sexual Communication: Speaking Your Sexual Truth

When I'm asked, what is the most important aspect of maintaining a healthy sex life?, I will always say, without hesitation, *sexual communication*. Without the ability to speak freely about what we like and dislike, and without the ability to listen to what our partners are wanting, we will most likely be lost in a bland and mechanical sexual routine.

Or worse, a couple will simply give up on sex altogether. This is an extremely common reaction to avoid dealing with sexual issues, especially as we get older. Ending the relationship is another frequent response to avoiding sexual issues. Some people assume that if their sex life with each other is poor, then they shouldn't be together.

While it is true that sometimes couples do need to separate, it is also true that just a few aspects of the relationship may need attention in order to rejuvenate things. Sometimes though, the desire to separate comes from a sheer fear of intimacy. It is very true that intimacy cannot be found and nourished without letting ourselves be vulnerable, and **although most human beings crave intimacy, the ego doesn't usually go toward intimacy willingly!** We end up fearing and avoiding that which we want the most: closeness, contact, and intimacy. No wonder so many people are unhappy!

It's a huge challenge to grow up in a negative sex culture and in spite of this, end up with good sexual communication skills. The odds are very much against us. So for most of us, it takes some conscious practise and attention to begin to feel more at ease with sex talk. One of the reasons I began to give talks on sex was because I saw that people needed role models to learn how to talk more freely about it.

If you are a person who has escaped negative sex conditioning and have no problem talking about personal issues with your sexual partner, then you can congratulate yourself and skip these next exercises.

But in my experience, most of us are timid and awkward in the sexual communication arena. Are you one of the multitudes of people who have difficulty talking about sexual matters? If so, then you will first need to overcome the discomfort about talking *generally* about sex. Only then will you be ready to tackle specific sexual issues with a partner. Please don't expect too much of yourself after years of negative sexual conditioning. Going too fast can cause unnecessary frustration and a desire to give up before you become comfortable being more open.

Exercise : Sharing Your Sexual History

Purpose: The goal of this exercise is to facilitate a habit of sexual openness.

Activity: This exercise requires your willingness to tell your sexual history. As before, use whatever format appropriate for you: journal, or share verbally with a friend or sexual partner. It can be done with a sexual partner at any time in the future so don't force it now if you aren't ready.

I emphasize this point because some less aware partners have a history of using sensitive material to have power over their partners, or will use it to embarrass or criticize them at a later date.

If you or your partner have such a history, then you may not feel safe yet to disclose more sensitive information. First, the trust issue needs to be addressed and resolved in some way. Until then, do the exercise with someone you do trust with this information.

In the meantime, acknowledge that the inability to trust your partner will certainly get in the way of good sex and will need to eventually be dealt with. Professional help may be required.

Naturally, it's not necessary to answer all the questions but notice the ones you avoid or want to avoid. Consider or share why you think it's difficult for you to go there.

Sexual History

Do you remember sex play as a child with other children? What do you remember doing? Did anyone know? Were there any consequences to it? Did you get in trouble? How did you feel about the experience then? How do you feel about it now?

_____

_____

_____

_____

_____

_____

Did you have any inappropriate sexual experiences as a child (sexual exploitation by an older person)? What happened? Did anyone find out? How do you remember feeling about it? Do you think you were affected by it? What do you feel about it now?

_____

_____

_____

_____

_____

_____

Are you aware of any incidents that caused sexual wounding?

_____

_____

_____

_____

_____

_____

_____

_____

Describe any early masturbation memories. How old were you? What did you do to pleasure yourself? Were there any negative or positive consequences? What messages were you aware of receiving about masturbation?

_____

_____

_____

_____

_____

_____

_____

_____

Describe your first adolescent or adult sexual experience.
Who was it with? Where were you? What did you do? How
did you feel about it? Were there any negative or positive
consequences?

_____

_____

_____

_____

_____

_____

_____

_____

_____

How many sexual partners have you had? How do you feel
about that number? What do you think it says about you as a
sexual person?

_____

_____

_____

_____

_____

_____

_____

Have you had partners whom you let affect your sexuality in a negative way? In a positive way? How?

_____

_____

_____

_____

_____

_____

_____

_____

Have you had any sexually transmitted diseases? Which ones? How did you get them and how did you treat them? How do you feel about it now?

_____

_____

_____

_____

_____

_____

_____

_____

_____

What sexual risks have you taken?

_____

_____

_____

_____

_____

_____

_____

_____

Have you been responsible about safe sex and contraception? Have your partners been responsible? Whose responsibility do you feel these issues are?

_____

_____

_____

_____

_____

_____

_____

_____

_____

_____

Describe any bisexual or homosexual experiences. How do you feel about them?

_____

_____

_____

_____

_____

_____

_____

_____

_____

_____

What are your biases about heterosexual, bisexual or homosexual people?

_____

_____

_____

_____

_____

_____

_____

_____

_____

_____

_____

Have you experienced anal sex? What do you think and feel about that form of intercourse?

_____

_____

_____

_____

_____

_____

_____

_____

What has your experience been with oral sex? How do you feel about it?

_____

_____

_____

_____

_____

_____

_____

_____

_____

_____

Is there any other information about your sexual history or beliefs that you would like to share?

_____

_____

_____

_____

_____

_____

_____

_____

_____

_____

_____

_____

_____

_____

_____

_____

_____

_____

Exercise: Sexual Honesty With a Current Sexual Partner

Purpose: To help you be more clear about which aspects of your lovemaking need nurturing, as well as to help you experience more ease in discussing sexual issues.

Activity: Each partner can fill out the following survey individually, then discuss it later. While discussing, remember to use "I feel..." statements as much as possible. Staying at a feeling level (thus avoiding blame and criticism) usually keeps the conversation from escalating into conflict.

Obviously, this exercise is only for people who are currently in a trusting sexual relationship, and who are committed and ready to be sexually honest. It can be done at any time so don't force it now if you aren't ready.

As in the previous exercise, if you or your partner has a history of using sensitive material to get back at the other person or have control over them, then get that resolved before doing the following exercise.

If you decide to do this exercise, remember that intimacy is the ability to show what's deep inside you. **One of the greatest benefits of communicating honestly and openly with someone is to be known and seen for exactly who you are. Only then can you truly relax with another person to the degree that is required to have great sex over the long term.**

Sexual Satisfaction Survey

Daily Life as Foreplay

I'm content with the amount and quality of kissing in our lives in general, as well as in our foreplay.

Very true   **True**   **Sometimes**   **Never**

I appreciate the overall level of affection in our lives, not just when we're asking for or expecting sex.

Very true   **True**   **Sometimes**   **Never**

We have ample variety of foreplay and are imaginative enough with sex games and various sexual scenarios.

Very true   **True**   **Sometimes**   **Never**

We create enough romantic experiences like special dates.

Very true   **True**   **Sometimes**   **Never**

We set the stage for sex by relaxing, bathing, listening to music, or doing sensual things like massage, anointing ourselves with scents or oils, etc.

Very true   **True**   **Sometimes**   **Never**

I'm satisfied with the amount we discuss or read about ways to enhance our sex with each other.

Very true   **True**   **Sometimes**   **Never**

We are respectful of each other's differing and fluctuating sex drives.

Very true   **True**   **Sometimes**   **Never**

We are good at stimulating other areas of the body besides the genitals during sex.

Very true   **True**   **Sometimes**   **Never**

I'm content with the level of experimentation (different types of sex, different places, different times) in our relationship.

Very true   **True**   **Sometimes**   **Never**

I'm happy with the amount of concentrated caressing of the sexual organs we receive and provide.

Very true   **True**   **Sometimes**   **Never**

Sexual Encounters

I think we make enough private time together for sex.

Very true   **True**   **Sometimes**   **Never**

We are good at knowing what we like sexually, and communicate this with each other comfortably.

Very true   **True**   **Sometimes**   **Never**

The length of time spent having intercourse is comfortable for me.

Very true   **True**   **Sometimes**   **Never**

I most often find intercourse enjoyable and comfortable.

Very true   **True**   **Sometimes**   **Never**

I'm satisfied with how often we have intercourse.

Very true   **True**   **Sometimes**   **Never**

I'm comfortable with the amount and type of body movement experienced during intercourse.

Very true   **True**   **Sometimes**   **Never**

The frequency and quality of orgasm during our sex together satisfies me.

Very true   **True**   **Sometimes**   **Never**

I'm satisfied with the variety of positions we use for intercourse.

Very true   **True**   **Sometimes**   **Never**

I'm satisfied with the number of times we repeat intercourse in one sexual encounter.

Very true   **True**   **Sometimes**   **Never**

Other Aspects of Sex

(If applicable) The way we handle contraception is adequate.

Very true   **True**   **Sometimes**   **Never**

I'm satisfied with the number of times we have orgasms by means other than intercourse, such as mouth genital or hands genital stimulation, for example.

Very true   **True**   **Sometimes**   **Never**

I'm satisfied with the way we investigate the potential of spiritual expression through sex, by reading, viewing, or conversing about it.

Very true   **True**   **Sometimes**   **Never**

I'm satisfied with the way we discuss emotional aspects of our sex life.

Very true   **True**   **Sometimes**   **Never**

I'm satisfied with the way we handle the issue of safe sex

Very true   **True**   **Sometimes**   **Never**

I'm satisfied with the level of affection/contact that happens between us right after sexual contact.

Very true   **True**   **Sometimes**   **Never**

I'm satisfied with the length of time we stay in contact after sex.

Very true   **True**   **Sometimes**   **Never**

I'm satisfied with the number of times we do something nice for each other after sex.

Very true   **True**   **Sometimes**   **Never**

I'm satisfied that we have created a different pattern for what we do following sex.

Very true   **True**   **Sometimes**   **Never**

9.

When Your Partner Says

"No Thanks"

How we handle the issue of rejection in our sexual relationships is incredibly important to the level of overall intimacy we can achieve with our partners. Everybody, at some time or another in the course of a long term relationship, will be both the instigator and the receiver of rejection. Sometimes, the longer we've been with a partner, the more ingrained and problematic our behaviour patterns around sexual rejection can become. Therefore, it is in our best interest to develop a healthy, open attitude about it.

Truly sharing ourselves sexually with another person is one of our most vulnerable interpersonal experiences. Very often, it is the fear of rejection that causes us to keep sexual secrets from our partners, and it can even cause us to avoid sexual contact altogether. To make matters worse, it's a topic that rarely gets talked about so most people feel quite isolated with their feelings. **Paradoxically, it seems that we're afraid to talk about our fear of rejection for fear of being rejected!** I'm sure you see the problem here.

When working with couples around sexual issues, I like to give them the rare opportunity to practise handling rejection in a fun and playful way. This allows them to be more at ease with it when one of them inevitably is rejected, instead of having the usual awkwardness and hurt feelings about it.

There are many general reasons why we fear rejection, for example:

♥ Fear of losing our connection to the other person.

♥ Fear that we're not good enough and might deserve rejection.

♥ Fear that the other person's lack of sexual interest relates to us in some way.

How many times have you decided not to initiate sex because you fear that your partner won't want to be sexual? In long term relationships, how a couple handles initiating sexual contact is of prime importance. Fear of rejection can play havoc with sexual desire when it is not acknowledged or discussed openly.

Consider the following case example which demonstrates a common dynamic between intimate couples (names have been changed).

Case Example

Lindsay and Sue had been together as an intimate couple for twenty years. Over the years, their sexual relationship had gone through the usual ebbs and flows but the couple felt that, overall, they'd had a satisfying relationship. However, when Lindsay reached age fifty, there was a noticeable dive in sex drive. Sue became the sole initiator for awhile to keep the sexual relationship going, but they didn't discuss with each other what was going on. When Lindsay refused sex, Sue felt rejected and took it personally, privately hurting herself. Each initiation became harder and harder until finally she quietly gave up suggesting that they have sex. Still, neither talked to the other about it. Hostilities grew. By the time this couple came to therapy, they hadn't had sex for three years. Sue had to come to terms with how she was hurting herself over Lindsay's reduction in sex drive. Lindsay decided to seek treatment for what turned out to be low testosterone levels. Over time, the couple learned to handle rejection in a more open way that helped them feel closer, rather than distant. Eventually, they began to have satisfying sex again.

What happened here? Sue hadn't acknowledged her feelings of rejection either to herself or to Lindsay. This caused considerable emotional distance. When Sue felt rejected she tried to ignore those feelings and hoped they would go away. But by not acknowledging her feelings or sharing them, hostility and distance developed, making sexual contact even less likely. I've seen variations of this scenario many times. Couples give up on sex far too easily, often due to their fears of rejection. So the more practiced you can be with handling sexual rejection, for example by communicating with your partner about your feelings, the better it will be for your relationship.

If you find yourself getting into a pattern of initiating most or all of the time, or you are feeling rejected, it is very important to talk about what's going on. If, for some reason, you don't feel safe doing so, please seek some help to change that situation. **You always have the choice to let your fear isolate you or have the potential to draw you closer together.**

Notes:

_____

_____

_____

_____

_____

_____

_____

Exercise: Handling Sexual Rejection

Purpose: To be aware of your role in the dynamic of sexual rejection.

Activity: Answer the following questions to get clear on your own attitudes about sexual rejection. Then, if you feel safe discussing this issue with your partner, do so.

In your sexual relationships, does one of you initiate sex more than the other? If so, why do you think that is?

_____

_____

_____

_____

_____

How do you handle sexual rejection?

_____

_____

_____

_____

_____

_____

What do you tell yourself when you initiate, and your partner doesn't want sex?

_____

_____

_____

_____

_____

_____

_____

_____

How do you imagine your partner feels when s/he isn't interested by your attempts to initiate?

_____

_____

_____

_____

_____

_____

_____

_____

How do you think your partner feels when you refuse sexual contact?

_____

_____

_____

_____

_____

How would you and your partner like to handle the issue of rejection differently?

_____

_____

_____

_____

_____

Is there anything preventing you from handling rejection differently?

_____

_____

_____

_____

_____

_____

_____

Are you committed to dealing with rejection differently? How?

_____

_____

_____

_____

_____

_____

_____

Notes:

_____

_____

_____

_____

_____

_____

_____

_____

_____

_____

_____

_____

Safe Sex

Safe sex is appropriate to discuss here because part of the reason we don't practise safe sex has to do with the issue of rejection. I continue to be surprised and appalled at the number of clients and friends who are ignoring all the information they have about the need for safe sex. These people understand the risk they take but take it anyway. These are intelligent, well-informed people!

The scope of this book is not to provide a thorough education on safe sex, however it seems appropriate to remind you of a few general rules we know. Remember...

♥ Any sexual contact carries some risk of sexually transmitted disease.

♥ Learn to use a condom.

♥ You are at higher risk if a person's sperm, penile fluid, vaginal fluid, blood, or excrement get onto another's mucous membranes or open wounds.

♥ You reduce this risk with condoms, dental dams, and latex gloves.

♥ Sexual diseases can be transmitted by both vaginal and anal sex.

♥ During oral sex, there may be lower risk for getting some sexually transmitted diseases, but a higher risk for spreading herpes, either from mouth to genitals or from genitals to mouth.

♥ Sexually transmitted diseases can be spread by using sex toys.

More extensive information is readily available at health units, in books, and on the Internet. If you think you need up to date information, please seek out those recourses. However, as mentioned before, the problem is not just ignorance. **The bigger problem is that we are not comfortable talking about sexual issues, nor are we willing to face sexual rejection openly.** Many people of all ages have told me that they don't want to make an issue of safe sex because their lover might be offended and reject them. Ultimately, fear of rejection is the culprit. Our need for acceptance outweighs our caring for ourselves.

Let me be clear that this conversation is not just directed at single people. When we look at the high incidence of sexual affairs in marriages, we have to face the fact that monogamous marriages are not exempt from sexually transmitted diseases and the need for safe sex. *The Kinsey Report* in the 1940s and 1950s showed that by age 40, 50% of the men had had an extramarital affair and about 26% of women. More recent, but less extensive research, suggests that the number of married people having affairs is actually much higher today. While I don't want to spread paranoia and suspicion, we do need to be realistic about the facts and act accordingly. The most powerful action we can take is to have open communication with our partners. So what are your attitudes about safe sex? Find out with the following exercise.

Exercise: Safe Sex Check-Up

Purpose: To be clear about your own attitude around sexual safety issues.

Activity: Finish the following sentences and, if you wish, discuss them.

I think practising safe sex means...

_____

_____

_____

_____

I think I need more information on...

_____

_____

_____

When it comes to talking about safe sex with my partner, I...

_____

_____

_____

_____

I'm afraid to deal assertively with safe sex issues because…

_____

_____

_____

_____

_____

I can improve my attitude about safe sex by…

_____

_____

_____

_____

I commit to changing my behavior regarding safe sex by…

_____

_____

_____

_____

_____

If you want to be more sexually assertive, but have trouble changing your behavior, please consider getting some help. Your very life may depend on it!

10.

The Magic of Breathing and Presence

"The way to do is to be."
—Lao Tsu from *Tao Te Ching*

Sexual communication is indeed the most important aspect of creating good sex, because good sex can't be sustained without it. However, when it comes to the physical mechanics of great sex, the skills of breathing and presence are the most basic and powerful.

What's the relationship between breathing and presence? The state of presence is what great sex requires; conscious breathing is how we can get to it. These are such important aspects of an evolving sex life that they each deserve special attention of their own.

Presence

The ability to stay present at anytime is one of the greatest challenges of being a human *being*, and that's because we get so wrapped up in the state of human *doing*. For example, even as I sit here writing about the state of presence, my mind creates many distractions and I have to stop myself from following them. Because I have a tendency to dissociate (i.e. not be present), one of my lifetime goals has been to work on becoming increasingly present. I have my work cut out for me!

Since we are all on a continuum which goes from being totally distracted to being fully present at any given moment, you are probably familiar with this concept. An extreme example of total distraction is a person with schizophrenia whose mind sometimes slips totally out of reality. An example of a fully present person would be an enlightened one; we all know they are extremely exceptional. So, other than rare enlightened individuals, very young children are our best models for presence, as they are often able to be totally engrossed (i.e. present) in any particular moment.

The following exercise helps you explore where you are on the presence continuum, during your sexual encounters?

Notes:

_____

_____

_____

_____

Exercise: Observing Your Ability for Sexual Presence

Purpose: To focus on your ability to be present during sexual activity.

Activity: Observe yourself during your next few sexual encounters. Then assess your own level of sexual presence by highlighting the statements below that apply to you. Then put an X on the presence continuum line on the next page to rate your general presence.

During sex, which of the following describes your level of presence?

♥ You are able to stay focused on your own physical experience.

♥ Your mind wanders when you have sex.

♥ Anxieties about different things get in the way of enjoyment.

♥ If anyone else is in the house, your mind gets focused on them instead of your experience.

♥ You're more focused on what your partner is thinking than on your own experience.

♥ You're wondering what it's like for your partner to feel the imperfections of your body (fat, wrinkles, moles, etc.).

♥ You're more concerned about how you smell than what you feel.

♥ You're wondering about your performance.

♥ You're thinking about tomorrow's dinner.

♥ You're wondering how long this is going to take.

♥ You've already moved on in your mind to the next activity.

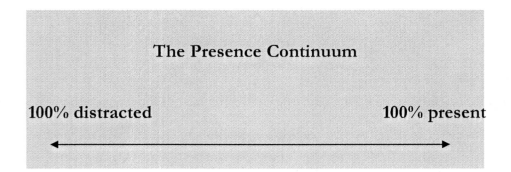

I haven't come across anyone yet who couldn't do with a lot of improvement in their level of presence (either during sex or in other parts of their lives). My personal thinking is that many of our problems in relationships, parenting, business, and even our health, stem from our inability to be present with ourselves and each other. That topic definitely requires a book in itself and has been well addressed in both, *The Power of Now* by Eckhart Tolle[32] and *The Presence Process* by M. Brown[33].

I encourage most of my clients to pursue their ability to stay present but especially clients who are having sexual difficulties. Many sexual difficulties are caused from our inability to be fully in our body, as well as our strong tendency to be wrapped up in the uncontrolled musings of our mind. The *Timeless Pleasure* CD which accompanies this workbook was designed to help you become more present.

Sex and the Breath

Of all the multitudes of personal growth and wellness techniques I've come across throughout my career as a therapist, I have found nothing as useful as the power of the breath! There are very good reasons why it is always the central factor in practices of higher consciousness like yoga, tai chi, meditation, and martial arts.

The power of the breath has been well known for centuries, yet still we are a society of poor and shallow breathers. Even though the concept of deep conscious breathing is simple, it's not that easy. That's mainly because it is normally an unconscious activity and moving anything from unconscious to conscious takes effort.

What makes breathing so powerful is the fact that it's a function of the body that can be either conscious or unconscious. By taking conscious control of an unconscious body function, we can drastically increase our control over body functions not normally under our conscious control. This is as true for our sexual function as it is for our overall health.

Like presence, breathing is a topic that deserves a publication of its own. If you want more information on breathing, I recommend Dr. Keith Jeffery's DVD, *4 Minute Fitness*[34] as well as the *Breathing* CD set by Dr. Andrew Weil.[35] Both these publications give a detailed description of the breathing process and how to increase your breathing capacity and control.

So why is breathing so important for high quality sex? Well, if you don't have the ability to stay present during sex, you limit your experience drastically. Breathing locates us in the body where the sensations are occurring, thus making them more intense. **With increased breath control, we can take more control over our excitement level, by consciously slowing the breath to avoid orgasm or quickening the breath to allow it.** Our habit of shallow breathing starts very early in life. If you look closely at how pre-school children breathe, you'll notice that they breathe from their diaphragm. This is the way we are designed. The abdomen moves up and down with each breath. Children are generally good models for healthy breathing.

We learn early in life (by about 7 years) that we can reduce or avoid uncomfortable feelings by making our breath shallow. This keeps us somewhat in our head and out of the body where the feelings actually are. As a defense mechanism, it works very well, but unfortunately, it becomes too habitual and limits our positive experience as well.

During sex, we want to be fully in the body because that's where the sensation is. Therefore, the habit of shallow breathing and getting distracted by our uncontrolled mind, are both issues that hinder high quality sex. Some other ways to use conscious breathing during sex are:

♥ To reduce anxiety

♥ To relax a muscle cramp

♥ To bring yourself into the experience of presence

♥ To slow the excitement down

♥ To intensify excitement

♥ To breathe into particular parts of the body to increase specific sensation (e.g. pelvis)

♥ To slow down ejaculation

♥ To intensify orgasm

So here are some simple ways to start working on making your breathing more conscious and controlled. This in turn will train you to be more present and have increased physical sensation. The pay off will be better overall sexual experience.

Exercise: Abdominal Breathing

Purpose: To practise comfortable, relaxed, and deep breathing into the pelvic region.

Activity: Lying on your back (this is an excellent thing to do when you can't sleep), put your hand on your abdomen. As you breathe in, let your abdomen rise up. As you breathe out, let it fall. Some breath teachers suggest breathing in through the nose and out through the mouth.

There are many different ways of breathing to discover. So to begin with choose the most comfortable method of exhale for you, through either your mouth or your nose. The most important thing is to relax enough to deepen the breath and get it more under conscious control.

As you breathe out, use your hand to push out all the air left in your lungs. Breathe out more than you usually would just for the purpose of this exercise. Breathe slowly and notice how often you can let your abdomen rise with the breath.

Throughout the day, begin to notice how often you are actually holding your breath or breathing very shallowly.

As you observed your breath throughout the day, what did you notice?

_____

_____

_____

_____

_____

Was the abdominal breathing exercise easy for you or an effort?

_____

_____

_____

_____

_____

What value can you see in consciously deepening your breathing? Will you do it?

_____

_____

_____

_____

_____

_____

_____

_____

Exercise: Harmonizing Breath

Purpose: To learn to synchronize your breath with your sexual partner. This activity is very nurturing, energy giving, and harmonizing.

♥   Lie in the spoon position with your partner.

♥   The partner on the inside is enveloped in the arms of the partner on the outside.

♥   Whoever feels most in need of nurturing (or is most energetically depleted) goes on the inside first.

♥   You should both be as comfortable as possible with your chakras or energy centers lined up together so you are as close as possible.

♥ If the person on the inside is feeling tension or pain near any one of the seven chakras (see Chapter 17), then the outside person can rest their hands over those spots. For example, if the inside person has a headache then the outside person could put one hand on the inside person's head and the other near their center, just under the belly button.

♥ Close your eyes, relax and breathe together.

♥ First, just breathe normally for a few minutes focusing on your breath.

♥ Then, consciously begin to pace your breathing with each other until you are using the same breathing pattern, inhale together, hold the breath together, exhale together, then hold the breath together again. This is usually experienced as gentle and relaxing.

Exercise: Reciprocal Breathing for Energizing

Purpose: To learn an energizing breath to use with a partner.

Activity:

If you wish to energize, you can do a form of reciprocal breathing. Lie in the spoon position as in the previous exercise. The outside partner consciously breathes out while the inside partner breathes in. Try some variations of the breath (deeper, more shallow, faster, and slower) As you experiment with this, you'll discover how each way gives you a very different result, thus providing a good demonstration of the power of your own breath.

This exercise is good to do after a hectic day, especially *before* attempting to be sexual. It's a good way just to connect anytime. After you have achieved more conscious use of your breath, breathing can easily be incorporated into sexual experience for the different sexual purposes mentioned earlier in this chapter.

What did you notice during this exercise?

_____

_____

_____

_____

_____

_____

Exercise: Observing Your Breath During Sex

Purpose: To become more conscious of the power of your breath during sex.

Activity: During a sexual encounter (alone or with a lover) notice what happens when you speed up, slow down, or hold your breath.

What did you notice when you increased the pace of your breath?

_____

_____

_____

_____

_____

What did you notice when you slowed and deepened your breath?

_____

_____

_____

_____

_____

_____

Did you hold your breath? If so, when? Did holding your breath intensify your experience or calm it?

_____

_____

_____

_____

_____

_____

While observing your breath more consciously during sex, what did you observe/experience?

_____

_____

_____

_____

_____

Some ways you think you can use this new awareness during your sexual encounters might be...

_____

_____

_____

_____

_____

11.

Overcoming Male Sexual Challenges

When Your Penis Has a Will of Its Own

If you have the desire for sex but other aspects of sexual functioning are getting in the way, you are not alone. We all have sexual functioning challenges from time to time. Those most common for men are discussed below.

Each of these challenges has very specific treatment and some can be eliminated quickly once they are admitted and investigated. Excellent books have been written on the treatment of sexual functioning issues. I recommend any of the works of Masters and Johnson[36], who did the most extensive sexual research into this topic. Meanwhile, I will touch briefly on several sexual functioning issues with the goal of helping you decide whether you need to look more closely into any particular one.

Erectile Inconsistency

The hardness of a man's penis is obviously an important matter, not just because of its role in sex but because it's a measure of his emotional and physical health. **Therefore, erectile difficulties are like a health barometer which informs a man when he needs to pay more attention to his fitness level (physical and emotional).** Hopefully, the ability to continue having sex is a good motivator toward a healthier lifestyle.

In regard to erection hardness, these are the following are the facts as we know them

Erections will usually be hard if:

- ♥ Blood vessels are healthy and elastic.
- ♥ Neural connections are working.
- ♥ Testosterone levels are balanced.
- ♥ Weight is controlled.
- ♥ Severe depression and/or anxiety are absent.
- ♥ Nitric oxide is being released in appropriate amounts through the body.
- ♥ No serious disease process is underway in the body.
- ♥ No medication is interfering with the erection process.
- ♥ There are no unresolved relationship issues.

Naturally, as a man ages, erection hardness will not be as dependable as when he was twenty. But research tells us that healthy men could have reliable erections well into their older years. The good news is that many men with erectile challenges can make lifestyle changes to lead them back to hardness. Meanwhile, more caressing of the penis and the use of a simple stretchy device called a "cockring" around the base of an erect penis will add to the level of engorgement and help erections last longer. For serious problems in this area, please start with a medical check up. And don't be afraid to ask about erection enhancing drugs.

The topic of erectile consistency requires a book in itself. A good resource is a new book called *The Hardness Factor*[37]. Dr. Lamm has mapped out a good six-week program back to sexual fitness, which covers all aspects of fitness related to erection ability. He understands that we have to practise prevention in regard to erection hardness, just as we do with other aspects of our health. He explains how the hardness of a man's penis can be suggestive of many common medical conditions including obesity, hypertension, depression, high blood pressure, diabetes, and heart disease. Healthy diet (omega 3s, more fruits and vegetables), exercise, and supplements (including pycnogenol, L-arginine, horny goat weed, grape seed extract, niacin, vitamin C and E) are all part of his well thought out *hardness regime*. And, of course, getting proper sleep and not smoking are both part of the hardness equation; it's all related!

So men, please don't be in denial about erectile health. Your life can depend on your paying attention to this barometer of your overall health. Here's your chance to take a good *hard* look at the issue.

Exercise: Evaluating Erection Dependability (Honestly!)

Purpose: To be open with yourself about your erectile function and to make a plan if necessary.

Activity: Circle the number that applies to you.

My erection is...
1 - Never dependable.
2 - Occasionally dependable.
3 - Somewhat dependable.
4 - Usually Dependable.
5 - Always Dependable (this is rare in most men).

From this I can conclude that...
1 - I need to take some action.
2 - I'm ready to take action.
3 - I need to see a physician.
4 - I need to do further reading on this subject.
5 - I'm great just the way I am (whew!).

I'm willing to take action on this issue!

Yes _____

No _____

Ejaculation Control

If you are challenged with poor ejaculatory control you are not alone. Some men have difficulty ejaculating too fast while others feel that it takes them too long. Still others sometimes can't ejaculate at all. Either way, it can be a real drag. The first step to ejaculatory control is to admit there is a problem because this is, in fact, a problem that can be easily remedied.

Exercise: Evaluating Ejaculatory Control (Honestly!)

Purpose: To be open with yourself about ejaculation issues, and to make a plan if necessary.

Activity: Circle the number that applies to you.

My ejaculation is...
1 - Never controlled.
2 - Occasionally controlled.
3 - Somewhat controlled.
4 - Usually controlled.
5 - Always controlled.

From this I can conclude that...
1 - I need to take some action.
2 - I'm ready to take action.
3 - I need to do further reading on this subject.

4 - I need to see a therapist or doctor.

5 - I'm great just the way I am (whew!).

I'm willing to take action on this issue!

Yes _____

No _____

Because... _____

_____

_____

If you are having difficulty ejaculating, you might want to get a physical and discuss this issue with your doctor. Also, check any medications you're using to see if they have sexual side effects. In particular, some common anti-depressants can make ejaculation difficult or impossible.

Premature ejaculation is a very subjective term since it is defined differently by various individuals. Still, it can be just as frustrating as the inability to ejaculate. Usually, it can be remedied by retraining the body's conditioned behaviors while learning to relax. It's quite possible that in many cases, men have trained their bodies to ejaculate quickly over years of hurried masturbating. As well, a childhood anxiety of getting caught masturbating can become attached to the ejaculatory process itself. When we add the possibility of performance anxiety to the sex act, control can become even more difficult. A vicious cycle can be perpetuated. So where does ejaculatory control start?

Masters and Johnson interviewed a thousand men with premature ejaculation during their research. They concluded that **the anxiety that men feel about this issue blocks the body's ability to have control over when they ejaculate**. Therefore, learning to relax is a useful part of dealing with ejaculatory control.

Exercising what is known as *the relaxation response* during sex is one way that men slow down ejaculation. It may be helpful to use the enclosed CD to condition your own relaxation response.

Another aid to create more control of your ejaculatory response is to use cockrings. Nowadays, specialized cockrings are made specifically for ejaculatory control. They inhibit the reflex that lifts up the testicles which occurs just before ejaculation, and they can be found at your local *sexcessory* store.

Masters and Johnson found that many couples can learn to improve ejaculatory control in as little as a couple of weeks using a technique called *the squeeze technique*. They found that this worked better with the help of a caring partner (doesn't everything!). For a complete description, I refer you to their book entitled *Heterosexuality*[38]. What follows is a brief description of their squeeze technique.

The Squeeze Technique

The partner uses the basic technique, first during experimentation (not during sexual activity), and later, during sex play when the man is aroused. The partner puts the pad of their thumb on the frenulum of the penis—an elastic band of tissue under the penis glans—while positioning the first and second fingers of the same hand on the opposite side of the penis (see below).

The Squeeze Technique

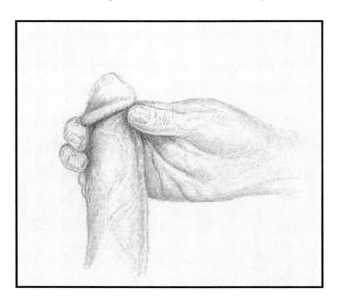

The first finger is put on the head of the penis (just above the ridge) and the second is placed parallel to the first but on the shaft of the penis (about a quarter of an inch below the ridge). The partner applies firm pressure for about four seconds.

Masters and Johnson suggested that when a couple decides to use this technique, it's necessary to suspend intercourse for a week or so and instead, plan on spending 30 to 40 minutes daily for several days engaging in purely sensual play. During this time, there is no intent to have intercourse or to orgasm. Instead, the partner simply uses the squeeze technique every few minutes whether the penis is erect or not.

Points to Keep in Mind with the Squeeze Technique

♥ Only use the pads of the thumb and fingers to avoid scratching and pinching.

♥ Only squeeze from front to back. Do not grip all around the penis.

♥ The pressure is proportionate to the level of erection.

♥ You can show your partner how much pressure is enough.

♥ There should be no pain involved.

♥ Practise on your own thumbs until you are comfortable with the right pressure.

♥ It's normal to create a slight reduction in penis hardness after the squeeze.

Steps to Ejaculatory Control

Step 1: Experiment with the right touch following the above suggestions until you are comfortable with what to do.

Step 2: For several days use the squeeze technique during 30 to 40 minutes of separate sensual play (taking turns of 15 to 20 minutes each). During this time there is no intent to have intercourse or to orgasm. Instead, the partner simply uses the squeeze every few minutes while directly involved with stimulating the penis, whether it is erect or not.

Step 3: As above, except the couple are stimulating each other at the same time rather than taking turns. This allows for double the sensation for the male to have to control. During this step there is still no intercourse, which reduces the pressure during the learning of a new skill. Continue to use the squeeze every 2 to 3 minutes. Make sure you have a few of these sessions before moving on to the next step.

Step 4: This step is designed to ease the man into *genital to genital* touching without having intercourse. Start with mutual touching for 5 to 10 minutes using the squeeze as before. Then if there is a full enough erection the partner can get into a position where the genitals are touching followed by the squeeze technique. The point is to have the man get comfortable with genital contact without having to ejaculate. When this is mastered you can go on to the next step.

Step 5: The goal of this step is to incorporate the squeeze technique into intercourse. It can only be successful if control has been achieved in the previous steps. Start with some sensual touching and caressing using the squeeze periodically. The assisting partner gets to be in a position of control (preferably on top) through the whole process. This allows the man who is learning the skill of ejaculatory control to be entirely focused on his own sensations. Masters and Johnson suggest that the assisting partner use the squeeze 3 to 6 times and once for sure, just before insertion. Lie still without thrusting. After 10 to 15 seconds of intercourse withdraw the penis and apply the squeeze before reinserting the penis again. Repeat intercourse but this time, after a few moments of stillness, the controlling partner can begin slow thrusting. Apply the squeeze before ejaculation occurs. When the man is able to resist ejaculation with thrusting for 3 to 4 minutes then allow the ejaculation to happen and celebrate. This process may have to be repeated several times or it may be successful the first time. Celebrate no matter what and enjoy the process.

Step 6: Continue to use the squeeze technique regularly for awhile as confidence builds. Once some control has been accomplished, the couple can use a modification where the penis is squeezed at the base where it attaches to the scrotum. The thumb is placed at the base of the penis and the first two fingers are parallel to the thumb on the other side. Pressure is always front to back not side to side. Hold for about 10 seconds when ejaculatory control is slipping away. This allows for eventual uninterrupted intercourse and either partner can do it. **Remember, control is a gradually learned skill that may come and go during the learning process.** You might as well enjoy the ride!

Men without partners can also work on this problem during self-pleasuring. Just don't be surprised to find that it may require a little more willpower and time. Keep at it, and stay encouraged.

Simplified Squeeze Technique with a Partner

Step 1

Learn and practise the technique outside of sex play.

Step 2

Use the technique while taking turns during sensual play.

Step 3

Use the technique during simultaneous sensual play.

Step 4

Use the squeeze technique while having genital to genital contact.

Step 5

Use the squeeze technique with your partner in control of intercourse.

12.

Overcoming Female Sexual Challenges

Entire books have already been written about the sexual challenges of women, so the purpose of this chapter isn't to be an encyclopedia of these challenges. Rather, it's meant to get you focused on dealing with any challenges that you might be avoiding. Each of the concerns below that are not discussed elsewhere in this workbook, will be covered in this chapter.

The most common sexual challenges reported by my clients are:

♥   Lack of desire (see Chapter 3)

♥   Inadequate lubrication.

♥   Pain during intercourse.

♥ Orgasmic difficulties (see Chapter 14)

♥ Vaginismus (involuntary spasm of the vaginal opening).

Lubrication: Don't Have Sex Without It!

Ouch! Inadequate lubrication can become a concern at any time in a woman's life, but it is more likely to occur at menopause. Usually, an imbalance in hormones is the cause, and this problem can easily be remedied by taking hormones or using a commercially available lubricant. I've seen women just stop having sex because of poor lubrication, but there is certainly no need to do that (unless, of course, you're looking for an excuse). Water-base and silicone lubricants are a pleasure to use for most women, and may even enhance their sensual experience. Oil-base lubricants are definitely not recommended! Among other things, they can destroy condoms and render them ineffectual.

The harder problem to deal with is when a woman isn't lubricating because of a relational issue or because of lack of sensual stimulation. If there isn't enough caring for one's partner or if there isn't sufficient foreplay to stimulate the glands, then there will likely be poor lubrication. Although men need to watch that there is enough lubrication before considering intercourse, women also need to be aware and assertive about communicating their level of readiness.

Dealing with Sexual Pain

Any amount of pain from intercourse needs to be investigated. It should be clearly understood that it is not *normal* to have *any* pain with intercourse. There are many possible causes and types of intercourse pain. It can be felt upon entry or deep inside the vagina. It can be occasional or regular. It can feel like burning, sensitivity, irritation, inflammation, or sharp pain. But whatever the pain symptoms, DO NOT PUT UP WITH IT. See your doctor and find out the source of any sexual pain. Here are some possible causes of pain during intercourse:

♥   Urinary infection.

♥   Inadequate lubrication.

♥   Vaginal infection.

♥   Genital irritation.

♥   Emotional issues.

♥   Arthritic pain.

♥   Tipped uterus.

♥   Endometriosis.

♥   Thinning of the vaginal wall at menopause.

♥   Drug side effects (can reduce lubrication).

♥ Lichen sclerosis.

♥ Cysts and tumors.

♥ PID (pelvic inflammatory disease).

♥ STD (sexually transmitted disease).

♥ Pain from other areas of the body.

♥ Vaginismus.

Unfortunately, as we age, pain during sex becomes more common though not necessarily from the sex itself. All forms of pain (arthritis, injuries, etc.) can limit sexual pleasure. Any pain that consistently occurs during sex needs discussing. So make sure you let your partner know what's going on for you. Otherwise, they may take your lack of response personally. There is usually a way to make you more comfortable if you plan ahead. The use of pillows, swings, and modifying positions to fit your body are a good start but each requires good communication.

Vaginismus

While some might think a tight vagina would be an asset…it can be too tight! Vaginismus is a curable physical and/or emotional condition that a small percentage of women experience. It involves an involuntary spasm of the muscles surrounding the vaginal opening, which makes intercourse either painful or impossible. It can be present during the first intercourse attempt or it can occur later in life. It often has obvious emotional roots. Treatment can be very successful and might involve both physical and emotional therapies such as couple therapy, kegel exercises, and the use of progressively larger vaginal dilators. Some massage therapists have been specifically trained to work with this problem as well. The most important thing is to seek help, and don't stop looking until you find it.

Exercise: Taking Stock of Sexual Challenges

Purpose: To bring to the foreground any sexual functioning challenges you might not be dealing with.

Activity: Think about or journal the answers to the following questions.

Are there any areas of sexual functioning that are challenging to you?

_____

_____

_____

_____

Do you feel you need medical help for any sexual challenges? If so, what are they?

_____

_____

_____

_____

_____

_____

_____

Think about, then list questions you have about your sexual functioning that you need to ask your doctor about, or investigate further.

_____

_____

_____

_____

_____

_____

_____

Are you committed to doing something to help your situation? If so, what? If no, why? What's stopping you?

_____

_____

_____

_____

_____

_____

_____

13.

Beyond Thrusting:

Developing Sexual Potential

Do you feel you are living your sexual potential? I've found that most people don't seem to comprehend such a concept. I think that's why so many couples either give up on sex or settle for mediocre sex. This isn't particularly surprising given that our culture is so poorly educated about sexual matters, and that there are still such taboos around talking about our sexual experiences. I believe we can seek to expand our sexual potential as we age, as long as we are willing to continue to redefine sex as our capacity dictates.

Most people, when asked, would say that they believe other people are having more and better sex than they are. Certainly the mass media and pornographic industry would confirm that idea, even though the type of sex depicted through the media is, in my opinion, still very limited in scope. Limited as it is, the media does make it seem like everyone is having great *worry-free* sex. That is extremely far from reality!

What I find so interesting is that, even though many people are dissatisfied with their sex lives, I rarely see people consciously working to improve it (readers of this book excluded of course!). They may be willing to work on health, fitness, finances, communication, etc., but rarely specifically on improving their sex.

I imagine the reason for this is that most people just don't realize that sexual development can continue throughout life. Also, a huge gap exists between what the media portrays as sexually normal, and what we tend to experience. This alone can make us feel inadequate, confused at the very least.
In fact, the media (particularly the pornography industry) communicates some harmful messages about sex that make it harder for us to be sexually open and honest. Perhaps men with ten inch penises and women always ready and eager for sex isn't exactly reality! We ought not to be intimidated by these fantasies.

Real sexual issues are not portrayed or discussed in Hollywood. You certainly don't see actors dealing with challenges like no lubrication, coming too fast, or not getting an erection, for example. No one jumps out of bed with leg cramps, and no one seems concerned at all about sexually transmitted diseases. And finally, they always have energy for sex! So, with all these messages, what can we expect of our sexuality in the real world we live in?

Sexual Potential

What exactly *is* our sexual potential, after all? I address this question from several different angles because sexual potential can be measured in mental, physical, emotional and spiritual contexts. For example, we can have physically gratifying sex and still feel lonely, isolated emotionally. We can also have emotionally satisfying sex and not have a fulfilling physical response. One is not better than the other because we have sex for many different reasons at different times. But when it comes to a discussion on sexual potential one needs to consider the various aspects of sexual experience.

Chapter 17 on *Sacred Sexuality* deals with the emotional and spiritual aspects of our sexuality, while the Chapter 4, *Developing your Best Sex-Positive Attitude* deals more with our sexual mind. So this chapter addresses the basics—the physical experience.

Physical Potential of Sexuality

On the physical level sex can only be as good as:

♥   Your ability to be present.

♥   Your ability to breathe consciously.

♥   Your understanding of human anatomy.

♥   The health and flexibility of your body.

♥   Your capacity to utilize all your senses.

With these five bases covered, the body has the capacity for great pleasures. But if there is a lack in any one area, the level of potential for sexual satisfaction is compromised. The first three on the list have been discussed in chapters of their own. The final two are addressed in the remainder of this chapter.

Health and Flexibility

Health and flexibility are essential components of good sex, and there are many books on the market that do a good job of educating you about health issues. Since being fit and flexible has such a strong influence on your sexual functioning, I want to get you thinking about your own commitment to health.

I'd like to think that the need to feed your body good nutrition goes without saying but what about flexibility, balance, and strength maintenance? What are you doing to maintain or improve those? If "nothing" is the answer, I recommend a baby step to get you started called *4 Minute Fitness*™ [39]. A short, mind–body, layered practice, it combines principles of Tai Chi, Qi Kung, Yoga, deep breathing, and medical visualization, and is taught in person or by video. You can find ordering instructions on the referenced website.

This unique approach explains the importance of practising your flexibility and balance daily to stop the common deterioration of these important abilities. Wherever your personal preference lies in exercise and stretching, just do it! Otherwise, your sexual expression will continue to be compromised as you age, which isn't really necessary! Take some action now if you aren't doing so already. It's never too late to start moving more.

Exercise: True or False Health Commitment Test

Purpose: To have you assess your commitment to meeting your body's physical needs.

Activity: Answer true or false.

I'm maintaining my body's muscle tone.

True____   False____

I'm working on developing and sustaining my body's flexibility and balance.   True____   False____

If the answer is false, what are you willing to commit to right now to look after these needs?

_____

_____

_____

_____

_____

_____

Pelvic Floor Fitness

Aside from general health, we also need to be specifically aware of keeping our pelvic muscles in good shape. The group of muscles that supports the pelvic floor in both men and women is called the pubococcygeus (PC) muscles. Not only do these muscles support our reproductive and other organs, without good tone in these muscles our sexual experience will be compromised. Specifically in regard to sexual activity for both men and women, the PC muscles are involved in intercourse, orgasm, and ejaculatory control. So obviously, the stronger they are, the better!

In both sexes, relaxing the PC muscles brings more blood to the genital tissue, which allows for more swelling and lubrication in women and stronger erections in men.
Fortunately, like any muscles, they can be strengthened at any point in our lives with some attention. This is good news because there is a definite correlation between PC muscle strength and orgasmic intensity. Who doesn't want that? While I've never had an orgasm I didn't like, stronger is definitely better!

How do you know what shape your PC muscles are in? Well, a well-toned muscle is one that you can contract and relax with ease. Both men and women can test their PC muscles quite easily by doing the following exercises usually referred to as *kegels* (after the gynecologist Dr. Arnold Kegel who designed the exercises for urinary incontinence in the 1940's).

Exercise: PC Workout

Purpose: To assess the strength level of your PC muscles and to give you a baseline for measuring the progress of any gradual strengthening of your pelvic floor over time.

Activity: When you are urinating, see if you can stop the flow of urine without squeezing your legs together. For some people this is an easy task. Others won't be able to stop the flow at all for a while.

Women who have had children may find it harder at first. The more you try, the sooner you will get the control to stop the flow of urine.

Exercise: PC Workout Pro

Purpose: To increase the strength of your PC muscles and intensify your sexual functioning.

Activities: Do these exercises gradually over time to increase your PC strength.

♥ Gradually increase the amount of time you are able to focus on the muscles that stop the urine flow.

♥ Contract and relax the PC muscles quickly.

♥ Contract the PC muscles and hold, gradually increasing the length of time before relaxing.

You can't really do this exercise too much. A good start would be to do them for ten repetitions, three times a day and gradually increase. The good news is you can do them anywhere once you get the gist of the exercise. Just think, you'll always have something to do in the bank line up from now on!

Personally, I find it a good activity to tie into some other activity I'm already doing in order to remember to do it. Initially, that can be when you're urinating, but eventually as you gain more control over the muscle it can be tied into any regular activity you are doing. For example, the following might be appropriate times to incorporate your practice into your life: when you bathe, shower, do yoga, or even when you lie down to sleep. Use whatever activity works best to remind you to do the exercises regularly.

When doing kegels in private, a woman can put her fingers in her vagina to feel the movement of the muscle and a man can put a finger on either side of the penis base. You can also use a mirror to watch the movement if you're not sure you're getting the right muscle group. And don't be concerned if your muscles tire easily at first. That is to be expected. Don't ever give up!

Sensory Awareness

Another aspect of physical sexual potential is developing and maintaining sensory awareness. We live in a culture where sensory overload is our everyday existence. We accept this experience as normal without questioning its impact on us. One of the repercussions of this situation is the gradual deadening of the senses. We must shut them down to some degree in order to survive and cope in a complex environment.

However, when it comes to expanding our sexual expression, we need to do the opposite of shutting our senses down. We want to allow our senses to work at their optimum level again, which requires developing conscious control over the sensory switch. The following exercise can help, and is a real treat you can give and receive from your lover.

Exercise: Awakening the Senses

Purpose: To help your partner learn to fully awaken and experience the five senses to become more sensually responsive.

Activity: Make a special date with your lover. You can keep the purpose of the date a surprise for full impact, or tell your partner what's going to happen if they have a strong need to know. You are going to provide a sensory awakening experience for your lover. It will require privacy and a block of uninterrupted time (a rare thing, I know!).

Preparation: You will need a blindfold to cover your partner's eyes to provide visual sensory deprivation. This allows a rest for the visual sense, which is typically over stimulated, and provides a fuller experience of the other senses. Next, collect articles to stimulate each of the other senses. Use whatever you have around the house and don't make it too complicated or you won't ever get around to doing it.

Here are some ideas to get you started:

Hearing:
Very different kinds of music; percussion instruments; rainmaker; crystal bowl tone recordings, or real bowls which will create different vibrational experiences on the body; didgeridoo recordings; other recorded sounds effects.

Smell:
Perfumes; spices; essential oils; flowers; vanilla; alcoholic drinks; incense; food flavorings.

Tactile:
Feathers; fur; silks; different kinds of stroking; non-sexual touch; fan; heating pad; ice; lotions or oils; foot massage; facial.

Taste:
Sweet; sour; salty; foods of different textures, smooth, hard, crunchy, etc.; whatever you have around the house.

Process: In a private place where you have set up all your props, blindfold your nude partner. The more you can use the element of surprise, the better. Begin with the awakening of one sense at a time. For example, present all the smells one after another, leaving time for observations and comments. This is meant to be a long and leisurely process—a great gift to be relished! As you slowly work your way through each sense, allow for full enjoyment. **Remind your partner often to breathe deeply to increase the intensity of sensory awareness.**

Because this experience brings you into deep contact with your partner, it can lead to an intense sexual experience but remember that's not the goal of this exercise. Instead, the goal is to learn to be more in the body and less in the mind so that your overall sexual expression is more satisfying. Go into the experience with no expectation of sex and just see what happens as you focus on sensory awareness rather than arousal and orgasm. Once your senses are fully awakened, do the following exercise to begin improving your physical sexual experience.

If you are motivated to start focusing on improving your physical sexual experience, I suggest you begin with the area in which you score the lowest. Later, after you've made good progress in that area, come back to this exercise to see what area of change you can focus on next.

Exercise: Physically I Need Work: Where Do I Start?

Purpose: To admit the area(s) of self-care that you may be ignoring.

Activity: As you contemplate your own ability to enjoy sex, strictly on a physical level, how would you rate yourself for each area?

	None	Fair		Excellent	
Your ability to be present in the body.	1	2	3	4	5
Your ability for conscious breathing.	1	2	3	4	5
Your understanding of human anatomy.	1	2	3	4	5

	None	Fair		Excellent	
The health and flexibility of your body.	1	2	3	4	5
Your capacity to utilize all your senses.	1	2	3	4	5

14.

Orgasm

"The six regions of the body
The five states
They all have left and gone
Totally erased
And in the open void
I am left
Amazed…
The Unobtainable Bliss
Has engulfed me…"

–Pattinattar, A. Tamil
The Poets of Powers,
Kamil V. Zwelebil, editor

Myth: Orgasm is the goal of sex.

While I've never had an orgasm I didn't like, there are lots of other reasons to have sex besides the desire to have an orgasm—to get pregnant, to feel close, to be giving, to soothe emotions, to cure a headache, to make-up, to name a few. If I believe this myth, then any sexual encounter I have where I don't have an orgasm would have to be considered *a failure*. What a set up that is!

Due to the very scientific study of sex, it has become linear in its conceptualization (i.e. foreplay leads to intercourse which leads to orgasm). This linear way of looking at sex needs to be re-constructed to fit reality. Lots of times we'll have foreplay with no intercourse. Other times, there will be intercourse with no orgasm. When we also consider having them in our dreams (yes, women too!), we see that we can also have orgasms without foreplay or stimulation of any kind. So one of the useful ways we can redefine sex is to accept that it can be any way we choose to define it. This will greatly reduce feelings of sexual inadequacy, failure, and frustration, especially as we age and our orgasmic potential changes.

Myth: The best orgasms in partner sex are simultaneous.

While it can be done, it's not all that common an experience. Actually, some people find that during simultaneous orgasm it's much harder to fully enjoy their own orgasm. This is partly due to the difficulty of keeping up the stimulation your partner needs, while surrendering to your own pleasure. The bottom line is that while it can be fun once in a while, we don't want anyone thinking it should *always* be that way.

Myth: For men, ejaculation is the only kind of orgasm.

Some men report the ability to have orgasm without ejaculation. It's usually described as an *energetic orgasm*. It is clearly distinct from ejaculation in that there is a release of tension but no ejaculation. In some sexual philosophies (e.g., Tantra, Taoist), this energetic orgasm is considered preferable to ejaculation because it builds energy, whereas ejaculation is seen to reduce it. In those disciplines men are encouraged to sometimes hold back on ejaculation and train themselves to enjoy energetic orgasm. This allows them to maintain their level of desire rather than have it reduced by ejaculation.

Myth: Women have only one kind of orgasm.

According to the responses from three thousand participants in the Hite Report (1981), women experience many forms of orgasm and describe them in a multitude of ways. They, too, can experience energetic orgasms which are experienced as overall body sensations, not specifically in the genital area. The point is, there is no right or wrong way to experience orgasm. Due to hormone fluctuations, a woman who is orgasmic one day may not be the next. In my opinion, there is too much importance associated with either being orgasmic or having the *right kind* of orgasm. That's what pressures women to lie about having them.

Myths: Orgasm isn't as important for women as it is for men.

While it's true that more women than men have difficulty achieving orgasm during sex with a partner, this issue is clearly important to women. It's also true that more women become simply resigned to not having orgasm during partner sex because it's more difficult for them to do so. However, most women who are not orgasmic during partner sex can easily achieve orgasm while masturbating. The Kinsey research found that most women could achieve orgasm while masturbating in an average of four minutes. Research has also shown that women who masturbate are more likely to achieve orgasm during partner sex.

Myth: Women should be able to have orgasms during intercourse.

Research has shown us clearly that intercourse is not the best way for the vast majority of women to achieve orgasm. The rhythmic friction of the clitoral system is simply not optimum in most intercourse positions. While it might be considered fun to keep trying, most women are simply not built for it. Fortunately, there are lots of other ways to stimulate women to orgasm.

Myth: If a woman isn't naturally orgasmic, there's nothing she can do.

Even though many women do not have orgasms during partner sex, the majority of those same women can have them by masturbating. During self-pleasuring they are obviously willing to experiment and utilize techniques that work. They have learned to stimulate the clitoris and the clitoral system, and most women find it easy to create an orgasm when they are in complete control of their experience.

For women who are not orgasmic at all *yet*, it's usually recommended that they learn to stimulate themselves through masturbation before trying to orgasm with a partner.

Even for those women who can orgasm while self-pleasuring but not during sex with their partner, it's *still* usually suggested that they self-pleasure and experiment more fully with what exactly excites them. The next step will be for them to communicate to their partner what works to help them achieve orgasm.

So use whatever sexual aids interest you in order to stimulate yourself, including erotic material, sex toys, music, lotions and oils, and any form of fantasy that helps you to create orgasm. Also, it would definitely be a good idea for non-orgasmic women to have their hormones checked as well as do the following exercise.

Notes:

_____

_____

_____

_____

_____

_____

Exercise: Problems with Orgasm during Partner Sex. (for women)

Purpose: To identify why you are not having orgasms.

Activity: Four of the most common reasons women don't have orgasms during sex with a partner are listed below. Highlight any that apply to you.

♥ Inability to say or show what they want.

♥ Inability to relax and surrender.

♥ Lack of anatomical understanding of the role of clitoral stimulation in building sexual energy to orgasm.

♥ Resentment is shutting down their sexual energy

Myth: There's nothing we can do to increase our orgasmic intensity.

Actually, there is lots we can do to increase orgasmic intensity. Keeping the pelvic floor muscles strong is a good start. As well, masturbation can be very useful to teach you how to reach orgasm, then how to strengthen and lengthen them. The average orgasm has been clocked by Masters and Johnson at four to twelve seconds (women's being longer than men's). Through the power of intention and specific sexual practice, orgasm can be both strengthened and lengthened consider

The Faking Orgasm Phenomenon

Proof that many women continue to have unsatisfactory sex is the fact that over 50% of women admit to lying about their sexual experience and faking their orgasms (Hite Report 1981). Other more recent surveys report up to 72%. A small number of men also fake orgasms although it's obviously a little harder for them to do so. **In my opinion, faking orgasm is a sign of a big problem in the way a person relates to him/herself and others both sexually and generally.**

I strongly believe that lying about anything in our intimate relationships creates distance. Sexual lies are no different. So, you might want to give some thought to the following question before your next sexual withhold or lie. Is your intention to create distance or closeness? If the answer is closeness, then buck up and stick to the truth. If the answer is distance, then at least have it be a conscious choice.

Notes:

_____

_____

_____

_____

_____

_____

Exercise: Why Lie About Orgasm?

Purpose: To explore some reasons you might lie about having orgasms.

Activity: So why do people lie? I ask my seminar participants this question at each seminar. The answers are always the same. Highlight those that apply to you.

♥ My partner feels responsible for my orgasm and I don't want to hurt his/her feelings.

♥ My partner feels disappointed if I don't have an orgasm.

♥ My partner will think I don't care for him/her.

♥ I want to be seen as sexually adequate.

♥ I'm not enjoying the sex but can't say so.

♥ I want the sex to stop but can't say so.

♥ I don't really know why I lie.

♥ Others?

_____

_____

_____

_____

_____

_____

Orgasmic Responsibility

All of the excuses we use for lying about orgasm are wrought with mistaken beliefs about orgasmic responsibility. The bottom line is that **we are all responsible for our own orgasm. Orgasm happens in our own bodies and is controlled by our own brains.** While good relationships and sensitive sexual technique obviously help us reach orgasm, it is the individual who ultimately allows or disallows it. If we all truly understood that, we wouldn't need to protect our partner's feelings so much.

In my seminars, I usually ask people if they would rather know the truth about their partner's orgasm, and only once did I ever have one man say he'd rather be lied to. When I asked him why, he replied, "Because it's easier that way." The rest of the participants said they would rather be *sensitively* told either what they could do to help their partner have an orgasm, or that they just didn't feel like having one.

Taking Control of Your Orgasmic Experience

In summary, here are a few things we know about orgasm and control:

♥ It's importance for many people to be in control of their own sexual experience, including orgasmic ability, as a prerequisite for satisfying sex.

♥ Many women have discovered what it takes to have an orgasm, but are not really willing or able to share that information with their sexual partners.

♥ Orgasm can be intensified if we are willing to cultivate our sexuality and take responsibility for it.

We know that when left to their own resources, most men and women can take control of their sexual experience and bring themselves to orgasm. So why are they not willing to share that information to improve their experience during partner sex? Is it simply old fashioned cultural conditioning? Whatever the cause, I know one thing for sure. **We can never be truly sexually liberated until we are willing to speak up!** Many of us have great reluctance to do so because of our cultural conditioning around discussing sex openly.

Exercise: Asking for What You Want

Purpose: To break the conditioning of not being able to say what you like and to practise saying what you like physically without having to do so sexually.

Activity: Ask your partner to give you a shoulder, face, or foot massage. Don't assume they will know how to do it. Instead, let them know that you will be directing them to massage you exactly as you would like it. If they are not using enough pressure, you will tell them to use more. If they are in the wrong spot, you will tell them to move to a specific location…and so on. Don't be afraid to actually show them the touch you want by demonstrating on their bodies. Take time and enjoy this process. Play!

After one partner has massaged the other, switch so you both experience having complete permission take control and ask for what you want. Afterward, ask yourself the following questions:

How well were you able to say what you wanted?

_____

_____

_____

_____

As the partner, what did you feel when you were asked to touch in a specific way?

_____

_____

_____

_____

Discuss with each other if there is any difference in saying what you want in a non-sexual massage and a sexual one? Why might that be?

_____

_____

_____

_____

_____

If either of you are experiencing hang-ups around asking for what you want sexually, consider discussing the following questions: Can this be changed? What will it take?

_____

_____

_____

_____

What are you willing to do to help with the issue of asking for what you want, or to make it easier for your partner to do so?

_____

_____

_____

_____

_____

What script of words can you say to yourself the next time the fear of being sexually assertive gets in the way of satisfying sex?

_____

_____

_____

_____

_____

Exercise: Strengthening Orgasm

Purpose: To experiment with having more orgasmic control with the intent of having stronger and longer-lasting orgasms.

Activity: During a self-pleasuring sexual experience, be conscious of how many times you can build sexual energy to the pre-orgasmic level and then back it off. It's easier to practice on your own first. This idea might be pretty foreign to you. Because orgasm is such a pleasant experience, we don't usually think of trying to stop it, but do this activity and see what happens. Consider the following questions while and after you experiment.

How well are you able to avoid actually letting the orgasm happen?

_____

_____

_____

What part does your breath play in the process? What happens when you slow down or speed up the breath?

_____

_____

_____

_____

What benefits do you notice from doing this exercise?

_____

_____

_____

_____

_____

_____

_____

_____

_____

_____

_____

_____

_____

You may want to feel competent at controlling your orgasms this way during self-pleasuring first. Then, incorporate this technique into your partner sex by teasing each other to excitement, but stopping just short of orgasm several times. You will soon notice stronger and longer-lasting orgasms. Entire books have been written on the subject of extending orgasm. It is a skill that can be worked on over your lifetime, as long as you are healthy (see Brauer and Brauer[40]).

Exercise: Setting Orgasmic Intention

Purpose: To explore and describe my personal issues around orgasm.

Activity: Complete the following questions honestly.

I would describe my orgasms as...

_____

_____

_____

When it comes to my orgasms, I'd like to...

_____

_____

_____

The following issues around orgasm have not yet been discussed with my sexual partner:

_____

_____

_____

_____

I'm avoiding discussing them because…

_____

_____

_____

_____

_____

_____

_____

_____

I commit to discussing them because…

_____

_____

_____

_____

_____

_____

_____

_____

_____

_____

15.

Keeping the Sexual Pot Boiling

Keeping the sexual pot boiling in long term, monogamous relationships is definitely a challenge regardless of how old we are. If you think that love is enough to fuel desire, you are sadly mistaken. While love can be a great aphrodisiac, it can only take desire so far. **Humans crave novelty and our desire begins to wane when we don't get it.** Each of us has to be responsible for keeping our own passion flowing. If you are blaming your partner for your own lack of passion, you are misdirecting your accusations. Look, instead, to yourself and take responsibility for your sexual experiences.

Keeping sexual desire alive for the same partner becomes even more challenging as we age. For the first time in the history of mankind, we find ourselves expecting to have long term monogamous relationships with good sex well into our senior years. This was not so at other times in history. People certainly didn't live as long as we do today, nor did they expect to be sexual in their latter years.

So What Can We Do?

First, we can accept the idea that our sexuality can continue to develop throughout our entire lives. We can never really stop being our sexual selves, even if we no longer engage in the *activity* we call sex. Our sexuality is who we are. So the first step is to continue to truly be who you are. In other words, continue to work on being your authentic self and continue to build your self-awareness until your last day on the planet.

Be personally responsible for your health. Don't leave your health in the hands of others. Be pro-active because your sex life can only be as healthy as your body. Along with maintaining a healthy lifestyle of good diet and exercise as discussed earlier in this book, both men and women need to be aware of any hormone or glandular imbalances. Deal with any pain management issues that are getting in the way of sexual enjoyment, and finally, keep those sexual (PC) muscles strong!

Continue to take personal risks and avoid getting into ruts. This will keep your life force flowing and readily available in the form of sexual energy, as explained in an earlier chapter.

Continue to take sexual risks. **Go ahead, be kinky, and don't worry, because it only seems kinky the first time.** As long as what you try is consensual, non-violent, and respectful, what can be wrong with it? Stretch yourself and be courageous in your commitment to pleasure. It is your birthright, after all!

As long as we live, there will be new experiences to try, both sexual and otherwise. If you think you've tried it all, try sexual experiences from earlier in your life over again, because something we experience in our thirty-year-old body will be entirely different in our sixty-year-old body. I cringe when I hear older people say, "I've tried it all!", because I know they've given up searching for new possibilities. That really is the end. Fortunately, you're not at that point or you wouldn't be reading this book!

You are never too old to take your sexuality to a new level. For those who still have desire, ability to be aroused and to achieve orgasm…appreciate your body for these abilities *daily* while providing it with a healthy lifestyle and new and novel sexual stimuli (see the following exercise) to keep these functions working. Use it or lose it!

For those of you whose desire, arousal, or orgasmic response are no longer dependable, you still have the ability to redefine sex according to whatever ability you do still have. In most cases, you can provide some sexual pleasure for yourselves and your partner regardless of your age or level of sexual functioning. Can you still kiss? Hug? Caress? Tell sexy stories? Fantasize? Massage? As we age, we need to focus on what abilities we still have rather than on those we don't.

Finally, do whatever you have to do to guard against taking your sexual partner for granted. This will kill desire almost more than any other factor. The next time you are sexual with your partner, try imagining that it could be the *last* time you make love to them.

We never know where our lives will lead or when they'll be over. In fact, each time really could be the last time. I discovered the value of this way of looking at sex from my own experience, and by talking to clients who were grieving. They reported that their sexual desire for their partners often increased while they were grieving the loss of another person. They used sex as a way to soothe themselves and noticed that the sex itself was much better than usual. Why was this? With each loss, we are faced with our own mortality. Each moment and experience can become intensified for a while.

You can consciously intensify your experience by bringing yourself fully into the moment any time. Act as though you may never experience it again because, of course, you won't. Each moment is unique, sacred, and never to be repeated. So make love as though it will be your last sexual opportunity and you'll see what I mean.

Exercise: Creating Sexual Novelty

Purpose: To help you focus on how to add sexual novelty to your love life.

Following is a limited list of ideas which can help create sexual novelty. During my training as a sex educator, I watched a film describing 500 of the most unusual sexual practices. It confirmed my suspicion that there is *nothing* people won't do in the name of pleasure, often including the sublime and ridiculous. I have purposely stayed on the conservative side of the scale with the ideas in this exercise. I do that because my experience has shown me that the majority of people are really quite non-adventurous sexually.

Activity: As you go through the following list of sexual novelty ideas, check the ideas you might be interested in trying. Note those you've already tried but might like to revisit, and finally, note which are out of your comfort range (perhaps highlight with different colors). If you have a sexual partner at this time, consider discussing why certain ideas make you uncomfortable. Are there any ideas you might want to explore? If you are on your own, consider journaling what you discover in this exercise, or talk about it with a close friend.

Expanding Sexual Experience

☐ **Setting the scene.**

Try paying more attention to setting the scene for great sex. Instead of just climbing into bed, think ahead. Use music, flowers, scents, props, or sensual lighting. **Lazy sex leads to mediocre sex.**

☐ **Seduction games.**

There is an art to seduction that goes well beyond foreplay. Once in a while, try making sex only about seduction. Extend the period usually referred to as *foreplay* into a long seduction game. Teasing is one of the most powerful ways to create intense arousal and build sexual energy. Lap dancing is a good example of a seduction game where the dancer teases with sexual movements and light touches but the receiver cannot touch the dancer.

☐ **Kissing.**

Kiss as many ways as you can think of, and give each other feedback on what you like best. Avoid tight-lip kissing as loose lips are more sensuous. Try running your tongue gently along the inside of your partner's lips, sucking lightly on the lip or tongue, circling each other's tongue with your tongue, etc. Why get stuck in a kissing rut? There are so many variations to explore. Move from the mouth area to the neck and any other part of the body. Visit erogenous zones you've discovered on your partner's body and free yourself to discover new ones.

☐ Massage.

Learning to massage your partner is a critical part of having good sex. We do not naturally know how to touch sensuously. We learn mainly through experience and feedback. As we age and lose some aspects of sexual functioning, this is one skill we will always be able to use. You can never learn enough about how to touch effectively. If you want to be a great lover, consider taking classes or reading books on massage, then enjoy practising it on your partner.

☐ Oils.

Oils are essential if you're starting your lovemaking with massage. But even if massage isn't in the picture, you can have fun by covering yourselves with oil and creating a novel sexual experience. Use lots and just have a spare sheet ready to handle the mess. It's well worth the extra laundry once in a while.

☐ Sensual games.

Gather a bunch of sensual objects (feathers, furs, flower petals, silk, etc.) and slowly caress your partner's body with them. Make it a gift. Have them just relax and enjoy the experience without any expectation that they have to please you. For your partner, this is practise *receiving* without obligation. For you, it is practise *giving* without expectation. Ask for feedback so you can learn even more about what your partner likes.

☐ **New positions.**

Most couples use a few tried and true positions that lead easily to orgasm. Get a book on sexual positions (there are many on the market), and make a goal to be more adventurous with each other. You'll be surprised what pleasures you can have in positions that allow for a variation in stimulation and energy movement.

☐ **Naughty sex.**

Of course, this means something different to everyone. But essentially, it means going over that line you draw that says "society won't sanction this behavior." We need to ask ourselves why "society" (whoever they are) has so much power over how we express our sexuality in the privacy of our own homes. Let's face it, for many people, the idea of being naughty is appealing, and we can give ourselves permission to explore as long as we keep it safe by communicating openly and honestly with our partners.

☐ **Using mirrors.**

Using mirrors stimulates our voyeuristic natures. It's kind of a safe way to have sex with other people in the room. It's a particular turn-on for people whose primary sense is visual.

☐ **Flashlight fun.**

This idea involves going under the blankets with a flashlight and getting a close up visual of the body parts you don't usually get to see. If you are a visual person, this will add to your excitement.

☐ Dress up.

Dressing in sexy clothes or in a costume to enhance a role play will be a turn-on for those with a strong visual sense. People that are more auditory or kinesthetic won't understand the attraction to dressing up, but they'll benefit anyway when the sexual energy gets intensified by adding this element to sex.

☐ Role-play.

Examples of ideas for role play would be: doctor, nurse, prostitute, nun, stranger, etc. (whatever works for you). Some couples find it stimulating to have a rendezvous away from home as though they are strangers meeting for the first time.

☐ Erotic material.

Erotic material can increase sexual desire for some lovers. People seem to either have a strong like or strong dislike for erotic books and films, and because of that, erotica has become a political issue. So all I'm going to say here is that sexual partners need to have open discussions about their attitudes and boundaries around erotica, and please...look at where your attitudes are coming from.

☐ Change the setting for sex.

If possible, take your sex life away from your bed from time to time. Use other furniture and props for sexual pleasure. Anything to change your routine will enhance sexual energy. Use other rooms of the house; outside locations...the sky's the limit.

☐ **Food fun.**

Food has many erotic aspects. Consider blindfolding your partner and giving them an erotic feast with a large variation of scrumptious taste sensations. Food can also be eaten off skin with lots of sensuous licking (chocolate, whipped cream, icing, etc.). This leads to a win-win situation.

☐ **Oral Sex.**

To be successful, oral sex requires three things: good communication, good hygiene, and good technique. Good technique can only develop over time between any two sexual partners, because lots of feedback is required for success. You are never an expert to start with. If you're unsure of different techniques to try, there are whole books written about this topic. But no book will replace communication. Simply ask, "What do you like?", and if your partner doesn't know the answer, explore and asking for feedback.

☐ **Dancing.**

Dancing either with a partner or for a partner has been a turn-on for people throughout the centuries. It also serves to get your body's energy moving, which will likely lead to more energetic sex. Dancing sensually can be a real stretch for many people. Is that a place you want to push yourself? Ask your partner if they would like it. Get some encouragement. Practise letting your body move to erotic music. Take lessons. Free yourself!

☐ **Anal sex.**

Practised throughout history, anal sex is still a taboo area for many. If you are new to anal sex remember the following pointers. Always practice safe sex (see Chapter 9) and discuss the topic thoroughly with your partner. Obviously, no one should feel pressured into having anal sex, and it won't work well if you can't relax. Empty bowels, good hygiene, a gentle attitude and lots of water based lubrication are key elements of success. Slowly build to gentle penetration using the finger first (see Chapter 5).

☐ **Finger penetration.**

Finger penetration can be very erotic for both the vagina and the anus. Make sure nails are trimmed, and remember, safe sex goes for fingers as well as for penises.

☐ **G-Spot exploration.**

Some women find G-Spot (see Chapter 5) stimulation very pleasing. Others do not. If you're curious about your own G-spot, but your partner's not interested in looking for it or you don't currently have a partner, there are many dildos and vibrators designed specifically to reach that area. Visit your local sex accessories store.

☐ **Prostate massage.**

The prostate gland is sometimes referred to as the male G-Spot (see Chapter 5). Some men find it erotic to have it digitally massaged internally. It can be gently accessed through the rectum, following safe sex rules and lots of *water based* lubrication. This activity requires a great deal of sensitivity and trust between partners. It may be initially uncomfortable and then gradually become more pleasurable as the anus relaxes.

☐ Sex toys.

Too many people are shy about, or even threatened by using sex toys during partner sex. Toys can help you have those novel sexual sensations that you need to keep your sex life alive. Consider having a collection of toys that you keep by your bed. Some ideas of toys to include would be; handcuffs, vibrators, blindfolds, soft ties, feathers, erotic edibles, mood music, and anything else that interests you. Please don't see them as competition. Sex toys are useful little helpers.

☐ Fantasy sharing.

There is such a thing as *fantasy sharing etiquette*. Introduce your fantasies gently, and make sure your partner knows that your fantasy is just a fantasy (see Chapter 7). It's wise to appreciate your partner sexually before introducing fantasy. Don't pressure your partner to partake in fantasy play when they are not comfortable, but instead, encourage talk about what makes them uncomfortable.

☐ Storytelling.

Lovers who are particularly auditory are turned on more by hearing about sex then seeing or feeling. They respond well to sexual storytelling, hearing sexual noises, or being read erotic material.

☐ Shower games.

Take a long sensuous shower together. Take extra time to lather and gently massage all parts of the body. Don't assume you'll know what your partner finds erotic. Ask for feedback about the way you are touching (You must be getting tired of hearing me emphasize this!). Allow them to guide your hand. They know themselves best. Encourage them to ask for what they want. That's both a secret and a prerequisite for great sex.

☐ Outdoor sex.

All I can say here is don't limit yourself. There are lots of safe places to have outdoor sex as long as you do a little scouting and planning.

☐ Ritual bathing.

Ritual bathing is more relaxing than shower games. It's a good opportunity to build anticipation for good things to come or as a sensual activity all on its own. Bathrooms can lend themselves well to romantic environments with a little help. Get the candles and soft music out. Wash each other in an honoring and humble way.

☐ Sexual ritual making.

Some people like to do various meditations or breathing exercises together to ritualize and add more meaning to their sexual union. Books on Tantric Sex are full of ideas about ritualizing sex.[41] This is a dimension of sex rarely developed in our culture since we do not generally hold much value in ritual. But adding ritual to any activity will intensify it. So if you want more intensity in your sex life, add more ritual and let Tantra teach you how.

☐ Harmonize the breath.

At the end of a hectic day, or especially if you or your partner are upset, lie together and consciously bring your breathing into the same pattern. This is a great way to come into connection with each other.

☐ Harmonize the chakras.

Lie on your left side in the spoon position. Synchronize your breathing using deep breaths. As one person names each chakra, visualize it being activated, starting with the Root chakra. On the in-breath, imagine pulling energy into the chakra. After four or five breaths move up to the next chakra until you reach the Crown chakra. Imagine your energies creating a warm loving field of energy and relax into this warm and loving space. If the idea of working with your chakras is new to you, see the enclosed CD, Track # 4 *Activating the Chakras*.

☐ Awaken the sense of smell.

Have an olfactory party by collecting all kinds of pleasant smelling objects and substances. Blindfold your partner and present him or her with each smell sensation. Do this slowly with a sense of ritual and gifting, with sensuous music in the background.

☐ Licking.

Some like to be licked some ways and not others. Find out what kind of licking your partner likes and where.

☐ Soul gazing.

Before beginning to have sex, try sitting across from each other and just look into each other's eyes. Making deep contact with your partner's soul through their eyes will increase your chances of a higher quality sexual experience with deeper connection. Or, do it instead of sex. It's a union of special intimacy at another level of experience.

☐ Make sex more sacred.

Having sex with more heart awareness and less genital awareness is one way to make sex more sacred. One of the best ways to do this is to give up your attachment to orgasm (at least occasionally). In Tantric philosophy it's believed that focusing on orgasm limits your erotic experience. Try letting go of the drive to orgasm, and instead, have a goal of lengthening your pleasure with more peaks and valleys.

☐ Power and control games.

Have you been tied up lately? Get yourself a pair of comfortable handcuffs or scarves for tying hands to each other or to the bedpost. This game fulfills the need for power and control that most of us have, whether we admit it or not. Sex is a wonderful way to *play* out those needs. Just make sure each of you gets a turn at both the power and submissive positions, and notice which one is the greatest turn-on for you. Also, for safety, agree on a signal that truly means "stop!", so you can enjoy your play acting all the more.

☐ Play voyeur.

Have fun playing at voyeuristic behaviors. Watch your partner self pleasure through the crack of an open door. Many people find this very erotic. Even though you both know the game is being played.

☐ Mutual masturbation.

Masturbation is not just a solitary activity. Pleasuring yourself in front of your partner is usually a turn-on for them. Make a special event out of it. Have a "no touching" period where you can't touch each other. This is a real tease and can be quite erotic.

☐ Hold off orgasm.

As you approach orgasm try relaxing into the heightened state of arousal by slowing your breath down and keeping your movement slow. Do this by slowing and deepening the breath. When you finally do decide to orgasm, try relaxing into it and focus on the energy pouring out of the crown of your head. Sometimes you will have energetic orgasms instead of, or as well as, ejaculations.

☐ Use breath for control.
The breath can be used to stimulate sexual energy or calm it. Generally speaking, breathing slowly will calm our energy and breathing faster will stimulate it. Try experimenting

consciously with this concept just to notice what control you do have.

☐ **Other Ideas?**

_____

_____

_____

_____

_____

_____

_____

_____

_____

_____

_____

_____

_____

_____

_____

Exercise: Sexual Experiences Out of My Comfort Zone

Purpose: To set clear sexual boundaries

Activity: List sexual activities you are not willing to try at the present time. Hopefully you are ready to share these boundaries.

_____

_____

_____

_____

_____

_____

_____

_____

_____

_____

_____

_____

_____

_____

_____

_____

Maintaining Sexual Energy in Long-term Relationships

Partners in long-term relationships want to know how to keep their sexual passion alive and replenished. Hidden sexual energy can be found, but we have to know where to look. **Most couples in healthy relationships search for passion in places of comfort, and surprisingly, we don't find it there**.

The issue of lagging sexual energy can show up early in life, but becomes even more of an issue as we age. Part of the problem is that in many intimate relationships we have done whatever we could do to create comfort. As nice as comfort is, it does dampen passion, and that's the truth! The following case scenario (names have been changed) demonstrates the negative consequence of a common pattern in long-term relationships.

Case Example

John and Mary, a couple in their early forties who had been married for twelve years, came to marriage counseling. Mary had grown up in a volatile home with lots of violent conflict. John's mother had been a single parent, so he didn't see any couple conflict resolution while he was growing up. So neither of them had good role modeling for how couples might handle the normal conflict found in all marriages.

During the assessment interview, it became evident that they had practically stopped having sex several years before, even though sex had been a very important part of their lives. They didn't know why. They described themselves as the best of friends. They never fought and felt they had a very good relationship, all things considered.

When I saw them separately, they confided that they did have some resentment toward the other person, but they felt these resentments weren't worth 'upsetting the applecart'. Clearly, they had an unconscious "no-conflict" agreement going on between them. Neither of them were willing to disclose their real feelings which might risk upsetting or losing the other. Therefore, their relationship of "best friends" was really built on fear, not love. Because they didn't know how to express resentments responsibly, they just never did. By withholding resentments they were not really being their authentic selves.

Unfortunately, by opting for comfort and avoiding potential anxiety or conflict, they effectively extinguished or repressed their sexual energy. Sadly, this is all too common a story!

Couples typically seek comfort and avoid anxiety. This is perfectly understandable because anxiety is uncomfortable to feel. But when anxiety is tolerated and managed, it can lead to personal growth, which creates the potential to deepen intimacy.

If we want continued sexual energy, it's important to look at how we might be selling ourselves out for comfort. For example, rigid rules about "conflict avoidance" will usually come along with low sexual energy, because the couple is avoiding intimacy by withholding. **Withholding in an intimate relationship dampens sexual passion!**

When we stop withholding, we create anxiety. You see the dilemma don't you? From this perspective sexual energy becomes a choice, and this choice is made by deciding between comfort and anxiety. Now you see why **maintaining your sex life takes committed attention and conscious desire. It requires a commitment to authenticity and true intimacy based on emotional honesty.** That's one of the reasons that we could be working on our sexual growth until the day we die.

We'll never be perfect at being authentic and emotionally honest. That requires eradicating the ego and most of us are a long way from that. It's odd that sex is seen as an activity for the young. The truth is that advanced sexual development can probably only be accomplished in our later years when we've somewhat tamed the ego!

Exercise: Deciding Your Sexual Future!

Purpose: To consciously create or co-create how you want your sex life to evolve as you age.

Activity: Complete the following sentences and create your future by deciding now what you want.

As I age, the vision I have for my sex life is…

_____

_____

_____

_____

_____

_____

I see I have dampened down my sexual energy in the following ways:

_____

_____

_____

_____

_____

What I plan to do about that in the future is...

_____

_____

_____

_____

_____

_____

_____

Notes:

_____

_____

_____

_____

_____

_____

_____

_____

_____

_____

_____

_____

16.

When Your Pubic Hair Turns Grey!

Our sexual development *can* extend from birth to death. I see it as gradual growth and expansion. Unfortunately, in the same way some people don't recognize that sexuality is part of childhood, they also don't recognize its role as we age. **The fact is, we are sexual beings from birth to death!**

All the chapters in this book are relevant to older lovers. Just because you are older doesn't mean you won't fall into all the regular sexual challenges experienced at earlier stages of sexual growth. This chapter, though, focuses on specific challenges that can occur when we're fortunate enough to live past middle age.

Popular media tends to communicate to us that sexuality is for young to middle age adults. Except for recent commercials for products that enhance erection, we rarely see older people being sexual, especially older women.

Often, people believe that our sex drive will, at some point, come to an abrupt end after which we will no longer have sex. But that's not the case. As long as the body is moderately healthy, our sex drive will diminish slowly and gradually until the end of life.

There are lots of myths that muddy our views on sex and aging. Following are some of the most destructive:

Myth: Older people aren't sexual.

All extensive research on sex and older people refutes this myth. Studies, like *The Starr-Weiner Report on Sex and Sexuality in the Mature Years* (1981)[42] and E. Brecher's *Love, Sex, and Aging* (1984)[43] have provided relevant information about sexual behavior and attitudes in the over-sixty age group. Older adults clearly have lots of interest in continuing their sexual expression as well as the ability to do so.

Myth: Having sex when you're old is immoral.

The sexuality of older people, like the sexuality of adolescents, frightens most adults in between. Older people have as much right to express their sexuality as anyone else. This bias is evident in many places, but especially in nursing homes where couples are often separated without considering their need for continued intimacy. Also, older individuals are often denied the privacy to self-pleasure if they are still sexually active. In fact, their sexuality is rarely discussed, giving them the false idea that perhaps it should be non-existent.

Myth: Elderly women are not sexual.

The idea of a sexy grandma is certainly not a culturally held vision. Yet, according to Brecher's *Love, Sex, and Aging,* the majority of women continue to have sex when they have an available partner and also pleasure themselves well into their senior years.

Myth: Sex can't really be as satisfying when we're older.

A National Council on Aging Survey reported that of those people having sex after 60, 72% considered their sex lives to be more satisfying then when they were 40.

The truth is that our sexual development will continue to expand as long as we are willing to work (or play) at it. As we age, changes in our bodies may cause us to make one of two choices: give up on sex (not recommended), or redefine it.

When you think about it, we do this redefining all the way through our lives. How we perceive sex at thirty is a very different from how we perceived it at sixteen. And that's a good thing! **The alternative to giving up on our sexual development as we age is to continue to allow it to thrive by redefining sexuality to suit our aging bodies, as well as our spiritual and emotional maturity.** After all, there are some very positive aspects to sex in later life.

Highlights of Sex Over Fifty, Sixty, Seventy!

♥ We have quite a lot more privacy at this point in our lives. If we've had children, they are, hopefully, gone and independent.

♥ There is no longer any risk of pregnancy.

♥ We've had lots of sexual experience by this time, and hopefully know our bodies really well.

♥ We have more time at this stage of our lives and usually feel less pressured.

♥ We've worked on our ego to the point that our ways of relating are more honest and authentic than when we were younger, allowing for much more depth in the sexual experience.

Even with these great advantages, **many couples can't get past the notion that the intensely passionate sex of their youth is the only "right" kind of sex, or the only kind of sex worth having.** They blame their sexual partner for not turning them on any longer (forgetting that we turn ourselves on!), or they blame their lengthy monogamous relationship for their lack of desire.

While there are certainly physical issues that impede sex over fifty, in many cases, it is often our sexual and emotional immaturity that leads to low sexual desire in our intimate relationships. Many people stop growing sexually and emotionally as they get older and are clinging to immature sexual fantasy. Rather than blaming monogamy for low desire, consider opening yourself to the possibility that in emotionally consider opening yourself to the possibility that in emotionally mature individuals, desire can be increased by familiarity and the risk of true intimacy.

From what I see in my counseling practice, many older couples would rather let their sex lives go than take the emotional risks necessary to help maintain it. This saddens me because sex can be such a pleasurable activity and so good for our health. But this book is obviously for those of you who are seeking to continue on with your sexual development. So let's take a few moments to look at some sexual issues particular to the aging process.

Issues of Sex over Fifty

Body Image

Because we live in a culture where youth is adored and aging is feared, we are conditioned to fear and detest the aging body. But being over fifty is a good time to let our sexual development begin to expand into a more spiritual dimension. As we increase our ability to see and love past the *physical*, we are maturing sexually (see Chapter 17). Couples that allow this transformation to occur exude a depth of love not available to younger lovers.

Andropause and Menopause

The change in hormones that occurs in both women and men after fifty can cause physical, emotional, sexual, and behaviour changes. Now, more than ever before, we have the ability and medical resources to deal with severe hormone imbalance. We now know that the adrenal glands, which are supposed to produce back up hormones later in life, are often exhausted (due to our hectic lifestyles) and can't produce what's needed to keep us sexually functional. But they, too, can be assisted. I would recommend a naturopathic doctor, compounding pharmacist, or a well-trained nutritionist for help if you suspect adrenal fatigue. If you suspect that a hormone imbalance is playing havoc with your sex life, don't just accept it as inevitable!

Erectile Issues

It's a fact of aging that the penis will not get as erect as often as it did in your youth. But anxiety over this fact seems to make this naturally occurring phenomenon into a full fledged problem and a *medical* diagnosis of *erectile dysfunction*. Fortunately today we have information, (see *Overcoming Male Sexual Challenges*) drugs, and devices that can help with erections as long as the desire is there. If this is an issue for you then ask your doctor for a referral to an expert in this area. Also, the simple use of a cockring (a stretchy band that goes around the base of the penis) helps keep blood in the penis.

Less Lubrication

Due to hormone changes, older women may have less vaginal lubrication. Fortunately, there are now many wonderful sexual lubricants on the market which can be used all through our sex lives. Hormone treatments have also helped many women restore their ability to lubricate effectively. Ask your doctor or pharmacist for reference material on hormone replacement. Lack of lubrication in itself is no reason to stop having sex. But some women use that excuse because they are not emotionally connected to their partners and don't want to be sexual with them. That's enough to reduce lubrication right there!

Longer Refractory Period

Yes, it's true that for men the time between ejaculating and being able to get another erection gets longer. So what! Just because sex doesn't happen as often as it did in the past does not mean that the quality of sex can't be as great or greater. In order to move on to a more mature level of sexual development, we all need to let go of our unrealistic expectations of our aging bodies. We can do what we can to stay in the best shape possible, and from that place we just accept and enjoy what is.

A new attitude about sex needs to be developed as we age that focuses on whatever potential for pleasure does exist. Satisfying sex does *not* depend on an absence of challenges and difficulties. Instead, it's about how we handle these difficulties. Do we handle them with frustration, or with a compassionate attitude? Do we avoid sex because it isn't what it used to be, or do we embrace each loving moment and make the most of it with a joyous heart? As we learn to overcome the challenges that aging presents, we can do it in a way that redefines our sexuality. At this age, you have more ability and opportunity to create even deeper intimacy and closeness than perhaps you had earlier in your relationships. Why not make the most of it?

Increased closeness requires both partners to honestly deal with the effects of aging on their sexuality, instead of the more common response of avoiding sex all together—a choice that unfortunately many aging lovers make, as the case example below demonstrates (names have been changed).

Case Example

Bob and Sue, a couple in their mid-sixties, presented with the problem of unprecedented anger toward each other. They were quite confused by this new development in their stable forty-five year old marriage. When questioned about their sexual life, they admitted they had gradually stopped having sex about a year before. Neither Bob nor Sue were really sure why and hadn't really questioned or discussed it. They had just let their sex life go, assuming that's just what happens when people get older.

When questioned further, it became clear that Bob had started taking an ulcer medication about the time that sexual activity ceased. Bob didn't know that this common medication could affect his desire and arousal ability and so never questioned his loss of desire, chalking it up to old age.

The couple's main way to make intimate contact had apparently been through sexual activity. When sex stopped, frustration mounted. Bob was encouraged to ask his physician for an alternative medication that didn't affect his desire. His medication change was successful. Once the couple started having sex again, their anger dissipated.

Exercise: Dealing with the Sexual Realities of Aging

Purpose: To help you decide to deal with any issues of sexuality and aging that you might be avoiding.

Activity: If you are past fifty and reading this book, I assume you are wondering what you can do to keep your sexuality healthy and expanding. Here are a few ideas to get you started. Perhaps you'll want to check those that apply to you.

Deal with any medical issues hindering sexual function. The longer you leave them, the harder they will be to deal with. Some common aging issues that impact sexual function are:

☐ Weight problems.

☐ Smoking.

☐ Flexibility issues.

☐ Erectile challenge.

☐ Hormone imbalance.

☐ Adrenal exhaustion.

☐ Lubrication issues.

☐ Medication adjustments.

☐ Pain management.

Talk with your sexual partner about concerns that you have about any changes in function. Keeping your concerns secret only adds anxiety. Good sexual communication is even more important as we age.

Sometimes it might be necessary to let go of your attachment to *having to orgasm* or *having to have intercourse.* You can still express yourself sexually without these functions.

Check your attitude about sex and aging. Are you feeling resentment, anger, or disappointment toward your body? Taking these feelings into sex will not help your cause. Your body is doing the best it can for you under the circumstances. Are you doing the best you can for your body?

Exercise: Troubleshooting Through the Aging Process

Purpose: To decide what you can do to keep your sex life healthy.

Activity: Think about and (if you wish) share answers to the following questions.

After going over the above list, what could you be doing to facilitate better sex while you age?

_____

_____

_____

_____

_____

_____

After looking at what you can do, what are you committed to doing?

_____

_____

_____

_____

_____

_____

_____

When and how?

_____

_____

_____

_____

_____

_____

_____

Sometimes having physical challenges with sex as we age can encourage us to focus more on the emotional or spiritual aspects of our sexuality. The next chapter explores what that actually means.

17.

Sacred Sex

The secret of sexual energy, therefore, is not only that it is capable of begetting new generations, but that it has a second function of much greater importance for man: to lead his consciousness step by step up the great Jacob's ladder of consciousness to God.

—Elizabeth Haich
Sexual Energy and Yoga

Much of what happens in our sexual experience goes far beyond the physical experience of our bodies. Is it emotional? Is it energetic? Is it spiritual? The truth is, it can be all of these things. Each time we are sexual our experience is different depending on our situation, our state, and most importantly, our intention.

While it's true that sometimes we may only be looking for physical release during sex, it's also true that sex can offer so much more. **As we open ourselves to the idea that our sexuality can take us into the spiritual realm, we are already creating new possibilities for ourselves.** My use of the term *spiritual* here simply refers to that which is nonphysical and not measurable in a physical way.

Some great works have already been published on the topic of sacred sexuality. I highly recommend any publications by Margo Anand. She has contributed a great deal to the introduction of Eastern principles of sacred sexuality to the West. As well, she has helped us gain an understanding of the role of energy in sex. In her three step process to creating ecstatic states, Anand has the following to say about energy and sex:

> Sex is first of all a matter of energy. The more energy you have, the more blissful you can be, the better sex becomes. In step one you learn to mobilize your energy and express it more fully until you experience orgasm as an "energy event" that can be learned and duplicated independent of the sexual context. In this process, you experience the essential part of orgasm, which I call the streaming reflex...as you experience the streaming reflex, you learn to welcome various kinds of vibrations and let them happen until they are felt as highly pleasurable.[44]

I have found that most of us are afraid of our body's energetic vibrations. When the body starts to vibrate we're afraid we're losing control. Partly, that's because the most common time for the vibration to occur is when we are having an emotional meltdown. This level of emotion terrifies most of us. Consequently, we have become very adept at shutting this vibration down. Initially, we do this in order to shut down uncomfortable emotions, but in doing so we inadvertently close the door to the full experience of our body's natural energies.

I remember the first time I became acutely aware of my own vibration. I was participating in a month-long personal growth program at *The Haven Institute*, when one day, out of the blue, my energy just let lose and my body began to vibrate, seemingly out of my control. It was soon pointed out to me, however, that the vibration was actually within my control and that I could shut it down at any point.

I learned that the vibration had always been there, but that I had been shutting it down habitually for years. However, in the safe environment of *The Haven*, I was encouraged to just let it be and observe it. This experience helped me become comfortable with the sensation so that I allowed it to happen when it occurred in other situations.

I was reminded that this vibration is our life force and that the more we are in touch with it, the better. After this experience, I found I could allow the vibration to get stronger anytime I intended it. It didn't need to be coupled with intense emotion and it can actually be used to energize and heal. It was like having a rheostat; I could turn it up or down at will. It didn't take long before I chose to let this vibration loose during sex, allowing for a much more intense experience. Years later, in a Tantra workshop, I learned that activating this vibration using breath and sexual energy was a Tantric technique.

I have often shared with clients, who are afraid of their own vibration, that in Tai Chi practice; years are spent cultivating this very experience. So rather than fear this vibration, we have the option to see it as a leap in our conscious awareness. The CD that accompanies this workbook, *Timeless Pleasure*, will help you experiment with allowing yourself to experience your body as energy. The more you allow yourself to experience this energy or *chi*, the more your sexual experience will be expanded beyond the purely physical realm.

I encourage anyone wishing to take their sexuality to a new level to investigate what Eastern philosophies (in particular Tantric and Taoist) have to offer in regard to learning to cultivate this valuable energy source. The language and extensive use of metaphor in Eastern philosophies may seem strange, but don't let that deter you from the valuable messages within. Sex can be a sacred experience which goes far beyond physical release. The study of Eastern philosophies helps us begin to understand that the **Western view of sexuality is both distorted and limited**. Most importantly, it becomes evident that we are grossly out of touch with the sacred aspects of lovemaking in our culture.

Thinking about sexual loving as sacred allows both partners to see themselves as divine beings and to be more in touch with their own true nature. This allows us to go beyond the limits of the personality, which cause so many problems in relationships, and instead allows us to create relationships on a higher level. Not surprisingly, this level of sexual expression is more available to the more mature adult who has learned to tame the ego. Does this type of sexual expansion interest you? If so, you might be interested in taking some time to read the following information about one of the Eastern philosophies that addresses the sacredness of sexuality.

What is Tantra?

Tantra refers to a series of esoteric Hindu books written over 2000 years ago. Although relics of Tantric rituals date back nearly five millennia, the 108 Tantric texts began to appear within a few centuries AD. Tantra offered a complete way of living and encompassed the material, physical, mental, psychological, and spiritual realms. The word, "tantra" simply means *expansion*.[45]

Tantric sciences included math, medicine, astronomy, sophisticated atomic time, space and sound wave theory, alchemy, palmistry, and astronomy. Tantra is credited with inventing the decimal system, discovering zero, and introducing the concept of chakras (see below). While Tantra is known as "the yoga of sex", the sexual element of Tantra was only a small part of its overall philosophy. Sexual love was considered sacred, and the ultimate goal of sex was unity or self-actualization.

Sacred Sex 101

You might be asking at this point what exactly do the words *sacred sex* mean. The concept itself is fairly foreign in Western culture. So, here are a few ideas from Tantra and other sacred sex philosophies. Perhaps you might want to highlight any ideas that you would like to incorporate into your own sexual practice.

♥   Tantric partners incorporate a lot of ritual into their lovemaking. Sex is treated as an activity with great conscious meaning. For example, special time is set aside for the ritual of lovemaking. Care is taken to attend to the environment in such a way as to stimulate all the senses. Sex is considered a "special" event to be cherished with ceremony.

♥ When coming together with the intent of making love, couples will honor the sacred aspects in each other. For example, they might say (or at least think) the word "namaste". Loosely translated this means, "I honor the sacred in you." One way or another, respect and honoring play a role in sacred sexual experience.

♥ Attention is paid to the aesthetics of lovemaking. Practitioners of Tantra are expected to be versed in the skills of conversation, dance, ceremony, massage, breathing, and meditation. These are known as the *erotic arts*.

♥ Tantra teaches lovers to consciously harmonize their energies using breathing and centering techniques, which is an important aspect of what we might call foreplay. It requires conscious breath control and the ability to experience and manipulate one's own energy.

♥ A prerequisite for Tantric sex is self-love. Trying to love another when you do not love yourself does not work. Sacred sexuality needs to start with you as an individual. For this reason, you do not need a partner to begin using sacred sex principles.

♥ Meditative activity is part of sacred sex. This will involve taking time to quiet the mind as part of sexual expression.

♥ A big part of Tantric sex is learning how to stream energy through the body using conscious awareness of the existence and function of the chakra energy centers. Lovers learn to move sexual energy from the genital area (2nd chakra) up through the body to create full body energetic orgasms (see *Timeless Pleasure* CD Track #4).

In summary, when we bless and honor each other as part of a sexual encounter, when we bond more deeply as a result of lovemaking, or when sexual energy catapults us into higher consciousness, we are experiencing sacred sex.

Exercise: Sacred Sex Self-Assessment

Purpose: To explore your feelings about the possibility of expanding your sexuality to include more sacred sex concepts and practices.

Activity: Consider, journal, and (if you wish) share the following questions.

Have you ever had feelings that your sexual practice is limited in scope or leaves you feeling empty? What have you attributed this to?

_____

_____

_____

_____

Do you feel there is a place for your spiritual development within your sexual expression? How would you see the two fitting together?

_____

_____

_____

_____

_____

_____

If you would like to explore the sacred aspect of your sexuality, what are you willing to do to get started? When are you willing to start it?

_____

_____

_____

_____

_____

_____

_____

_____

_____

_____

_____

Chakras 101

So what exactly are chakras? There are various models of chakras from different traditions. The word comes from the Sanskrit "cakra" which means "wheel, circle", and sometimes refers to the "wheel of life". While there are differences in interpreting the function of chakra energy, there seems to be general agreement that the seven main chakras exist in a column from the base of the spine to the top of the head.

Each chakra corresponds to a specific part of the body and is associated with a certain color, function, and element of consciousness (see chart below). They are "connected to each other and to portions of physical-cellular structure via fine subtle-energetic channels known as nadis which distribute the life force and energy of each chakra into the physical body."[46] The seven major chakras are described below. However, there are numerous minor chakras as well as meridians that are involved in our energetic bodies. For a complete discussion on this topic see Barbara Brennan's book, *Hands of Light.*[47]

Although the existence of chakras has been known and written about in ancient texts for thousands of years, there has only been scientific proof of their existence since the 1970's (see Hunt[48] and Motoyama and Brown[49]). The locations of the seven major chakras seen below correspond to the major nerve plexuses of the physical body in that area. They can be open or closed and have a great influence on our health and ability to experience pleasure.

Learning to open the chakras by generating sexual energy is a goal of Tantric sex and is considered to be very healing. But they can also be opened by doing body work or with concentrated intention. It is believed that for full body orgasm to occur all chakras need to be open so that energy can move freely through them. Tantric sex teaches these skills.

While most people cannot see chakra energy, we have all experienced it. As you look at the location of the seven major chakras you will see that each is the center of strong sensations. They are depicted through our language as follows: "I thought my heart would burst."(4th chakra), "I had a lump in my throat."(5th chakra), "butterflies in my stomach"(3rd chakra), "a strong feeling of arousal"(1st and 2nd chakra).

It's been said that chakras are like the strings on a guitar. Each one vibrates at a different frequency. When the chakras are in tune we are in a state of harmony like a well-tuned instrument. More and more, westerners are beginning to understand the power of their own energy systems, both in creating vitality in sex and also in maintaining good health. Although awareness of chakra energy showed up first in body work therapies like Healing Touch and Reiki, it is appearing today in most healing professions.

In my own profession, the field of Energy Psychology has become very popular because of the success of its energy techniques, using both chakra and meridian energy-based systems. In my own healing process, I've found them to be most effective and have now embraced them in my counselling practice. I highly recommend the use of these techniques for those of you working on changing limiting core beliefs or compulsive behaviour. For further information on the use of energy techniques in psychological work, go to www.energypsych.org[50]).

If you are interested in learning to sense and work with your own major chakras, Track #4 on the enclosed *Timeless Pleasure* CD will be useful.

Location of Major Chakras

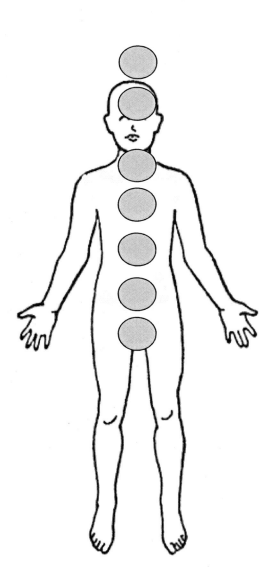

Crown Chakra
Spiritual Connection

Third Eye Chakra
Inner vision

Throat Chakra
Governs communication

Heart Chakra
Governs Respiration and Heart

Third Chakra
Emotional Center

Second Chakra
Sexuality & Creativity

Root Chakra (Base of Spine)
Survival & Instinct

(See the color associated with each chakra on the front cover.)

Exercise: Body as Energy

Purpose: To experiment with experiencing your body's energy or chi.

Activity: Listen to Tracks #2, #3, and #4 on the *Timeless Pleasure* CD, then consider, write about or share the following questions.

Were you able to become more aware of your body's energy? If so what did you experience?

_____

_____

_____

_____

_____

_____

_____

_____

_____

_____

_____

_____

_____

_____

Were you aware of ways you allowed or disallowed this energy to be more noticeable?

_____

_____

_____

_____

_____

_____

Do you have any questions you want to follow up on in regard to this energy and how it might be experimented with during sexual activity? How will you do it?

_____

_____

_____

_____

_____

_____

_____

_____

_____

_____

_____

Sacred sex philosophy is something that you can continue to expand and play with until the end of your human experience. When it comes to expressing our sexuality we can never truthfully say, "We've done it all." That would just be showing our ignorance of the possibilities that exist. Clearly, most of us have only begun to explore the full parameters of our sexual potential. There will always be more to discover.

It's my sincerest desire that you have been able to use this kit to create more pleasure and deeper connection in your life. I hope you have been encouraged to continue with the development of your sexuality until the end of your experience on earth. For that is indeed your birthright!

Namaste!

Appendix A

Timeless Pleasure CD (Track #5)

Suggestions for a Positive Sex Attitude

Pleasure is a gift of being human.
My body was designed for pleasure.
It's ok to be sexual with myself.
Sex is just another aspect of myself.
Sexual energy is life energy.
It's safe for my sexual energy to move.
I am responsible for my own sexual energy.
My sexuality is who I am.
I'm free to give myself pleasure.
It's okay to turn myself on.
I'll never be too old to be sexual.
My sexuality is healthy.
I open myself to all that is good.
It's safe to be in my body.
My body is a gift.
I am meant to use my body respectfully.
It's healthy to be sexual.
Sex is good for my health.
It's healthy and safe to have sexual desire.
Good people can be sexual people.
Giving pleasure is a pleasure.
I deserve pleasure like everyone else.
I'm responsible with my desire.
It's safe to express myself sexually.

I have healthy sexual boundaries.
I can let myself receive pleasure no matter how I look or feel.
Pleasure is my birthright.
I am responsible for my own sexual pleasure.
It's healthy to allow myself pleasure.
I'm loveable the way I am.
I am a sexual being.
It's okay to be a sexual being.
I am strong and sexually capable.
It's okay to ask for what I want.
The more I ask for what I want, the more I can enjoy
It's okay to speak openly about sex.
The more I can speak openly about sex, the better it gets.
The more pleasure I have, the happier and healthier I am.
We are all sexual beings, from birth to death.
The older I get, the more sexually capable I am.
Because I am a loving human being, I am a good lover.
The more I learn about sexuality, the better lover I am.
It's okay to make sex a priority among other important aspects of my life.
I am a sexual being like all humans.
I'm open to achieving my full sexual potential
I'm ready to expand my sexual experience.
I know sexual development is endless.

Endnotes

Chapter 3

[1] Judith Reichman, M.D., *I'm not in the Mood* (New York: Quill, 1998).

[2] Ibid., 38.

Chapter 5

[3] W. Masters and V. Johnson, *Heterosexuality* (New York: Harper Collins, 1994).

[4] Alfred C. Kinsey, Wardell B. Pomeroy, Clyde E. Martin, and Paul H. Gebhard, *Sexual Behavior in the Human Female* (Philadelphia: W.B. Saunders, 1953), 584.

[5] Shere Hite, *The Hite Report* (New York: Dell, 1976, 1981), 179.

[6] June M. Reinisch and Ruth Beasley, *The Kinsey Institute New Report on Sex,* (New York: St. Martin's, 1990), 201.

[7] Robert T. Michael, John H. Gagnon, Edward O. Laumann, and Gina Kolata, *Sex in America Survey: A Definitive Survey* (Boston: Little Brown, 1994), 128.

[8] Edward M. Brecher, *The Sex Researchers* (New York: Signet Books, 1969), 214-15.

[9] Ibid., 214-15.

[10] Cathy Winks, *The G-Spot* (San Francisco: Down There Press, 1998).

[11] E. Gräfenberg, "The G-Spot and other Recent Discoveries about Human Sexuality," *International Journal of Sexology* (1950).

[12] Ibid.

[13] Federation of Feminist Women's Health Centers, *A New View of a Woman's Body* (Simon & Schuster, New York, 1981), 47.

[14] E. Gräfenberg, "The G-Spot and other Recent Discoveries about Human Sexuality," *International Journal of Sexology* (1950).

[15] Cathy Winks, *The G-Spot* (San Francisco: Down There Press, 1998), 33.

[16] Milan Zaviacic and Beverly Whipple, "Update on the Female Prostate and the Phenomenon of Female Ejaculation," *The Journal of Sex Research* 30 (May 1993): 148-51.

[17] Gary Schubach, "Urethral Expulsions during Sexual Arousal and Bladder Catheterization in Seven Human Females," (Doctoral research project, Institute for Advanced Study of Human Sexuality, San Francisco,.1996), 39.

Chapter 6

[18] E. Holt, *The Diseases of Infancy and Childhood: for the Use of Students and Practitioners of Medicine* (Originally published in New York: D. Appleton, 1897).

[19] E. Erickson, *Childhood and Society,* second, revised and enlarged edition (New York: W.W. Norton, 1963).

[20] D., Frankel, "US Surgeon Forced to Resign," *Lancet* 34 (1994): 1695.

[21] D. Greydannus and B. Geller, "Masturbation: Historic Perspective," *New York Journal of Medicine* (November 1980).

[22] E. Brecher, *The Sex Researchers* (San Francisco: Specific Press, 2000).

[23] Ibid., 147.

[24] Ibid., 59.

[25] Ibid., 65.

[26] Ibid., 182-84.

[27] Alfred C. Kinsey, Wardell B. Pomeroy, and Clyde E. Martin, *Sexual Behavior in the Human Male* (Philadelphia: W. B. Saunders 1948), and

Alfred C. Kinsey, Wardell B. Pomeroy, Clyde E. Martin, and Paul H. Gebhard, *Sexual Behavior in the Human Female* (Philadelphia: W.B. Saunders, 1953)

[28] E. Brecher, *The Sex Researchers* (San Francisco: Specific Press, 2000), 296.

[29] Ibid., 311.

[30] Shere Hite, *The Hite Report on Male Sexuality* (New York: Ballentine, 1982), and

Shere Hite, *The Hite Report on Female Sexuality* (New York: Dell, 1976).

[31] June Reinish, *The Kinsey Institute New Report on Sex* (New York: St. Martin, 1980), 229.

Chapter 10

[32] Eckhart Tolle, *The Power of Now* (California: New World Library, 2004).

[33] M. Brown, *The Presence Process* (Vancouver: Namaste, 2005).

[34] Keith Jeffery, *4 Minute Fitness Video* (www.4minutefitness.com, 2002).

[35] Andrew Weil, MD, *Breathing, The Master Key to Self Healing* (Boulder Colorado: Sounds True Recording, www.soundstrue.com, 1999).

Chapter 11

[36]W. Masters and V. Johnson, *Human Sexual Inadequacy* (Boston: Little Brown, 1970), and

W. Masters and V. Johnson, *Heterosexuality* (New York: Harper Collins, 1994).

[37]Steven Lamm, MD, *The Hardness Factor* (New York: Harper Collins, 2005).

[38] W. Masters and V. Johnson, *Heterosexuality* (Boston: Little Brown, 1970, and New York: Harper Collins, 1994), 108.

Chapter 13

[39] Jeffery, Keith, *4 Minute Fitness Video* (www.4minutefitness.com, 2002).

Chapter 14

[40] A. Brauer and D. Brauer, *ESO—How You and Your Lover Can Give Each Other Hours of Extended Sexual Orgasm* (New York: Warner, 1989).

Chapter 16

[41] Cassandra Lorius, *100 nights of Tantric Sex* (London: Harper Collins, 2002).

[42] *The Starr-Weiner Report on Sex and Sexuality in the Mature Years* (New York: McGraw-Hill, 1981).

[43] E. M. Brecher, *Love, Sex and Aging* (Boston: Little Brown, 1984).

Chapter 17

[44] Margo Anand, *The Art of Sexual Ecstasy* (New York: G.P. Putnam's Sons, 1989), 28.

[45] Charles Muir and Caroline Muir, *Tantra: The Art of Conscious Loving* (San Francisco: Mercury House, 1989).

[46] R. Gerber, *Vibrational Medicine: New Choices for Healing Ourselves through the Human Energy Field* (New York: Bantam, 1997).

[47] B. Brennan, *Hands of Light* (New York: Bantam, 1988).

[48] "Electronic Evidence of Auras, Chakras in UCLA Study," *Brain/Mind Bulletin* March (1978): 77-8.

[49] H. Motoyama, *Science and the Evolution of Consciousness: Chakras, Ki, and Psi,* Brookline, MA, (Random House, 1978).

[50] Association for Comprehensive Energy Psychology website, www.energypsych.org.

Thank you for using this toolkit. I hope it was useful in leading to more love and pleasure in your life.

If you have any comments or questions please don't hesitate to email me at krisanna@krisanna.com.

If you would like to be put on an email list for notifications about upcoming Great Sex for Life workshops or coaching, just email me with the word workshops/coaching in the subject line. Your address will then be added to an email list which will only be used for this purpose.